Puzzlegrams Too!
A further colourful collection of
puzzles devised by Ivan Moscovich,
designed by Pentagram.

   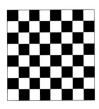 

STANLEY PAUL

First published 1994

Design by David Hillman
and Emily Chow
Pentagram Design
Text by David Gibbs

1 3 5 7 9 10 8 6 4 2
Copyright © Pentagram Design Ltd
and Ivan Moscovich 1994

First published in the United Kingdom
in 1994 by Stanley Paul & Co. Ltd
Random House, 20 Vauxhall Bridge Road,
London SW1V 2SA

Random House Australia Pty Limited
20 Alfred Street, Milsons Point, Sydney,
New South Wales 2061, Australia

Random House New Zealand Limited
18 Poland Road, Glenfield, Auckland 10,
New Zealand

Random House South Africa (Pty) Limited
PO Box 337, Bergvlei, South Africa

Random House UK Reg. No. 954009

A CIP catalogue record for this book is
available from the British Library

ISBN 0 09 178547 2

Printed in Great Britain by
Butler & Tanner Ltd, Frome and London

Cerebral and intuitive puzzles test
your patience, your concentration
and your self-esteem. You have
to decide whether to think before
you jump, or jump before you think –
it's up to you.

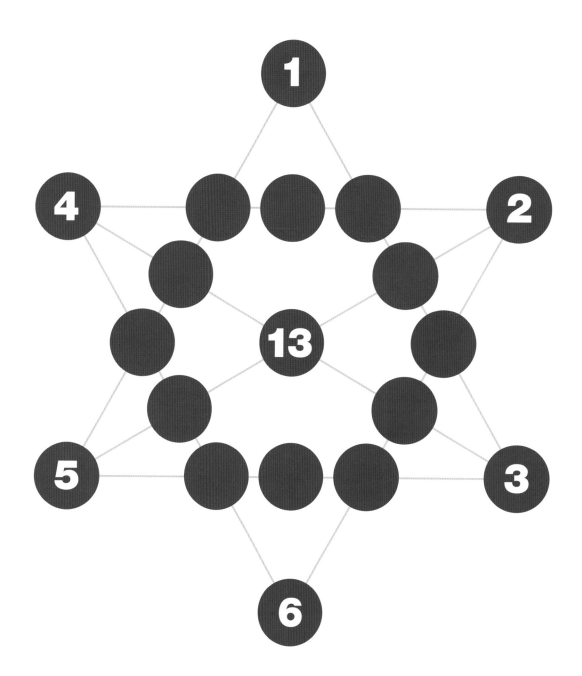

Star Ratings
Place the numbers 1 to 19 in the
circles of the six-pointed star so that
the sum of the numbers in each
straight line adds up to 46.

Hidden Triangles   7
How many triangles of different
sizes can you find in this hexagonal
pattern?

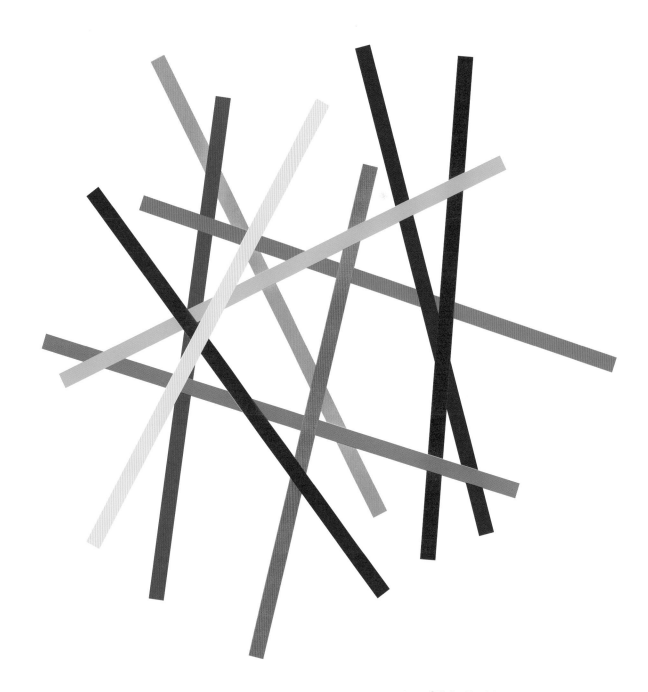

8

Sticky Problem
Imagine removing each of the
coloured sticks one-by-one from the
top of the pile downwards. In what
colour sequence would the whole
pile be cleared?

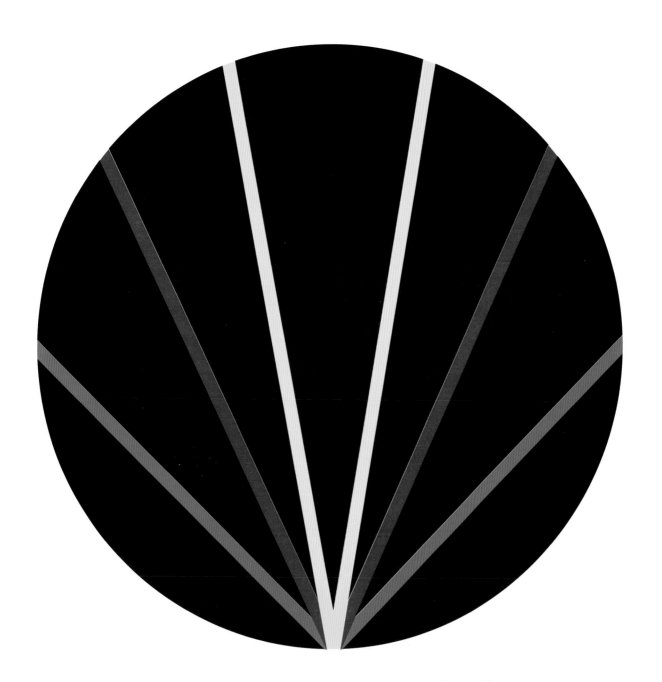

Moving Lines 9

Imagine the wheel cut out and
balanced on the point of a pencil and
given a spin. Guess what will happen
to the 6 coloured lines when the
wheel revolves?

Castle Cover
Move the castle around the
chessboard so that it visits all
the squares in 16 moves.

Patch Work
Using six colours, fill in the squares of a 6-by-6 grid so that no colour appears more than once in any row or any column.

11

Knot or Not
Could the elements of this
arrangement be separated without
cutting, or not?

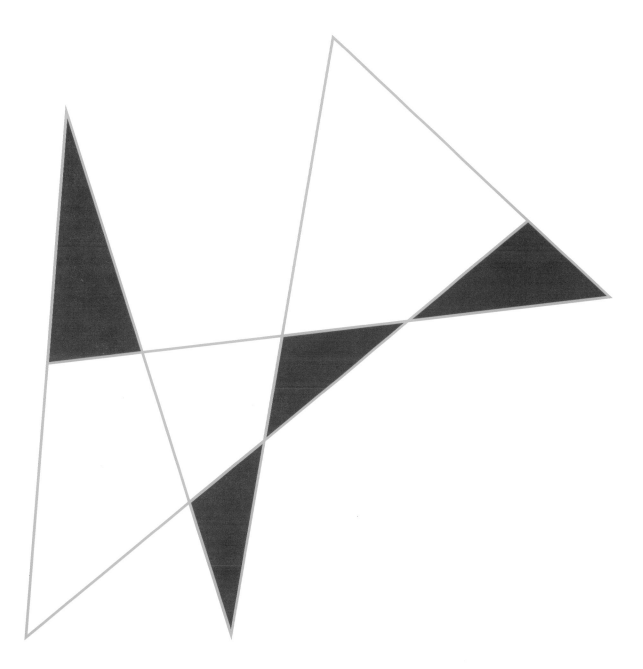

Six-line Triangles   **13**
Four triangles have been created by
six straight lines. Can you do better
and create a seven-triangle solution?

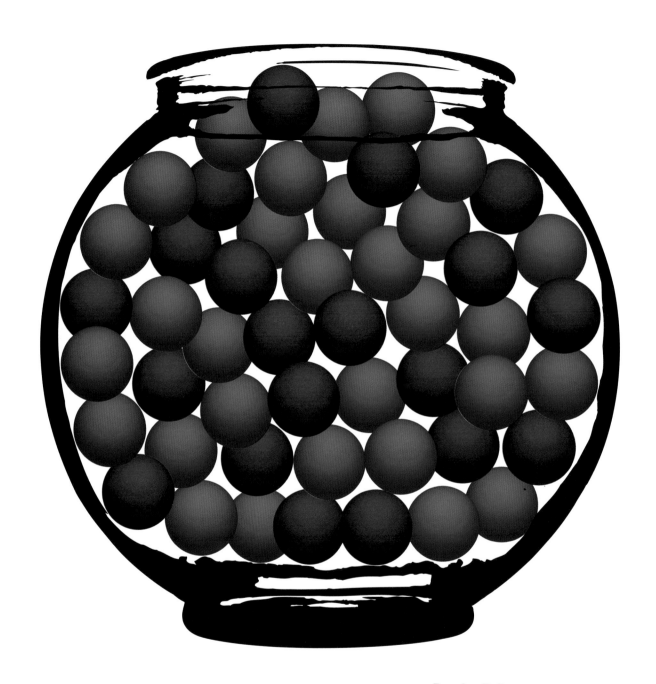

14

Drawing Balls
A container holds 20 red balls and
30 blue balls. If you take out a ball,
what is the probability of it being:
a red ball; a blue ball?

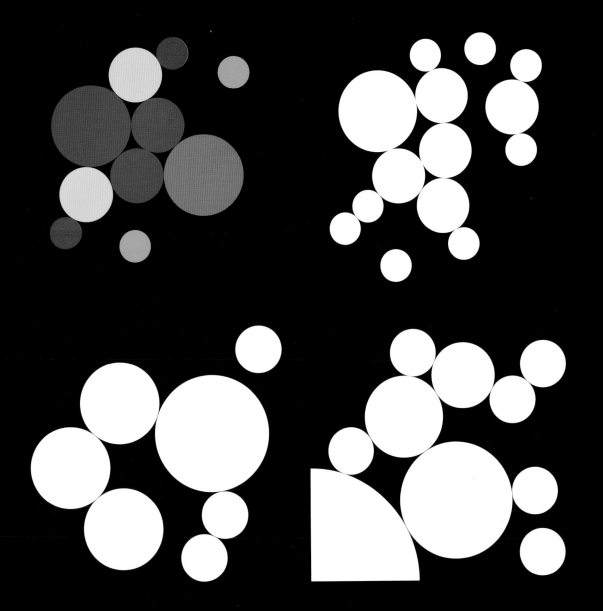

Colour Ways   **15**
Discover the logic of the colouring
of the first figure and then fill in the
colours of the other three figures
accordingly.

Jailhouse Walk

Nine prisoners are taken for their daily exercise handcuffed together in threes. How would the warder arrange the men each day so that no two men are handcuffed together more than once over a six day period?

18 27 6 4 12 9

The Right Order
Find a logical sequence using all
the numbers above.

Paper Weight
How can you suspend a brick
with a piece of thin paper?

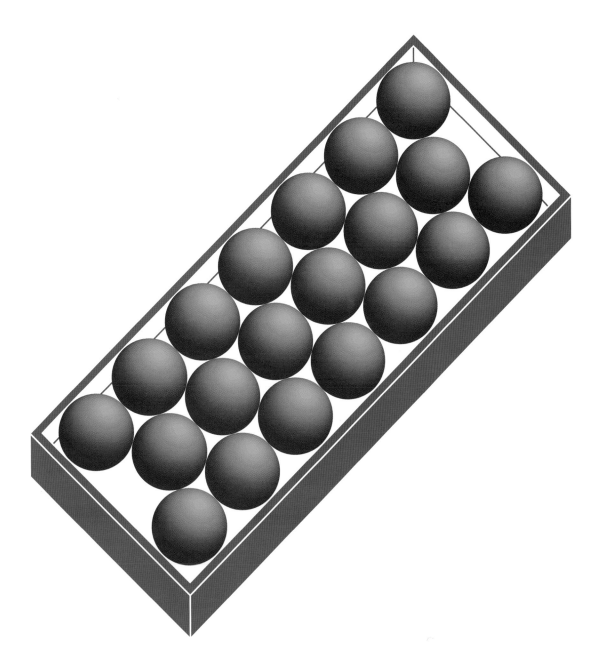

Balls' Box   **19**

How many balls can be removed
from the box so that you can still
rearrange the remainder to make
a tight fit?

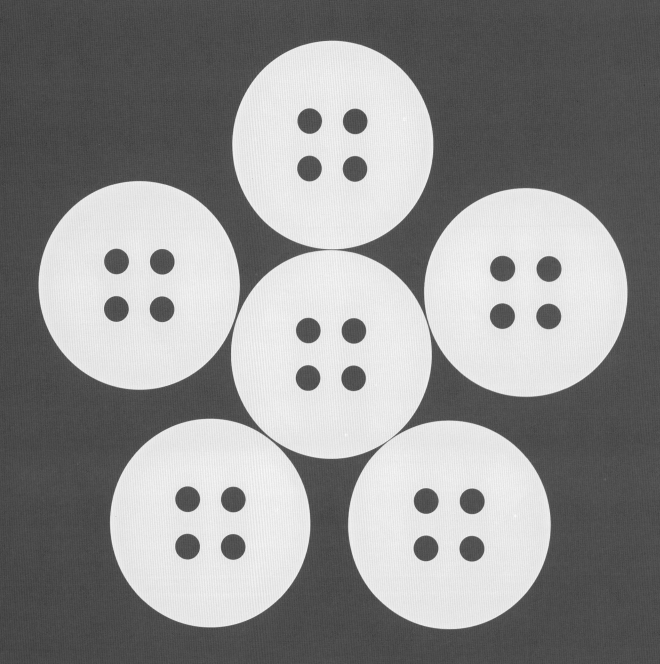

Push Buttons
Arrange six buttons in the pattern above. You are allowed to move the buttons by sliding one at a time without disturbing any other and so that it ends up by touching two other buttons. How many of these moves do you have to make to end up with the pattern on the left?

Dot Matrix   21

Colour in the dots so that you end
up with the same number of dots
in any row or any column or along
either diagonal.

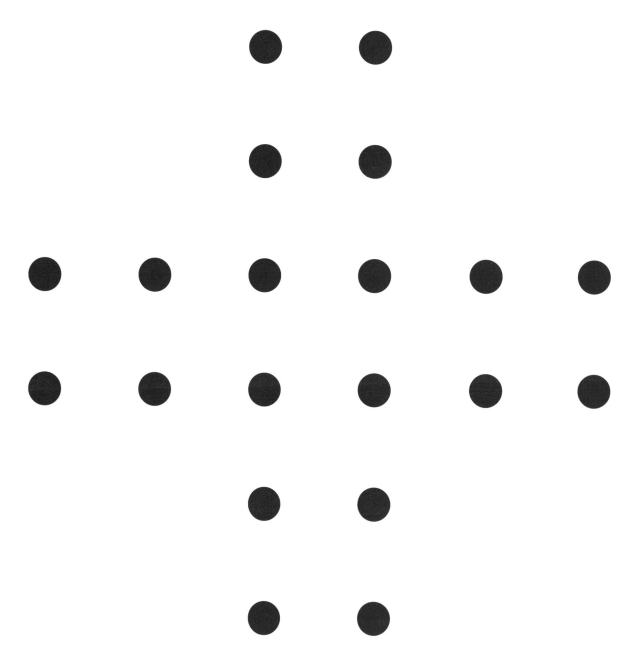

Dotty Squares
Make as many squares as possible
by connecting any four dots for each
square.

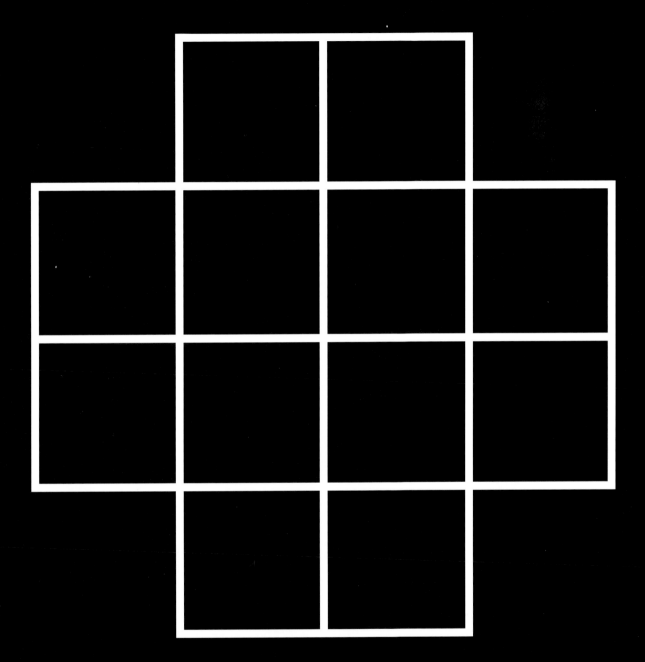

Line Management
The board of squares is made up of 32 individual lines. Can you colour in the lines, five in red, seven in blue, nine in orange and eleven in green so that each colour is continuous and does not cross over another colour? You should end up with all the lines on the board coloured in.

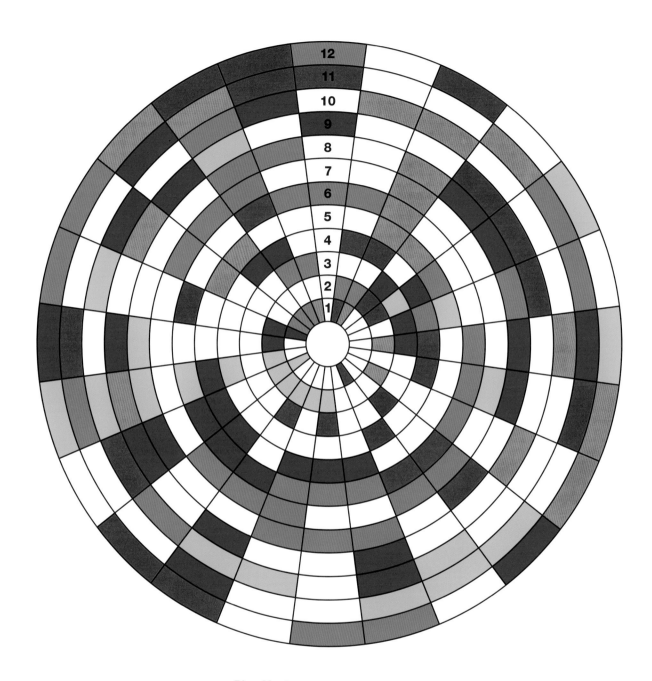

Ring Master

Imagine these concentric rings can be moved round independently. In order to create a continuous radial line in one colour running from the outside to the centre, which rings would you move and which colour would the radial line be?

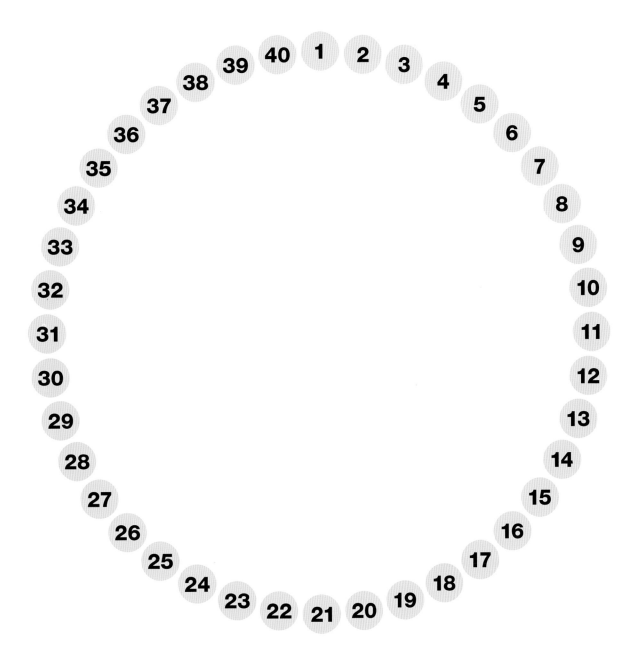

Your Circle of Friends

Imagine yourself and 39 friends in a circle. Counting from number 1, every third person is removed (so number 3 is the first to go). If you were to continue in this way around the circle as many times as necessary, which two numbers would you pick so that you and one other friend were the only ones left after the rest had been eliminated?

26

The Long Walk
Trace the longest route possible
through the maze without going
along any part twice and without
crossing your route.

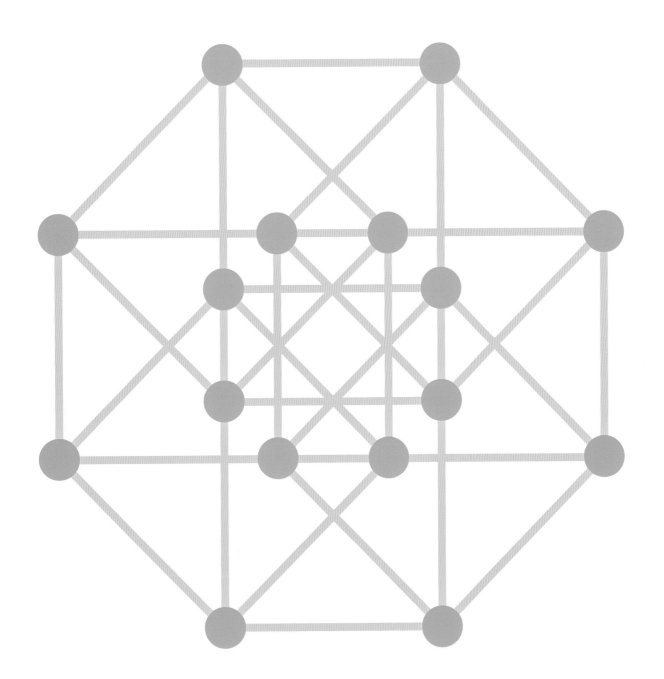

 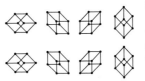

Cube Addition

Fit the numbers from 0 to 15 in the circled points of the 'hypercube' so that the numbers on the square faces of the eight cubes in perspective add up to 30.

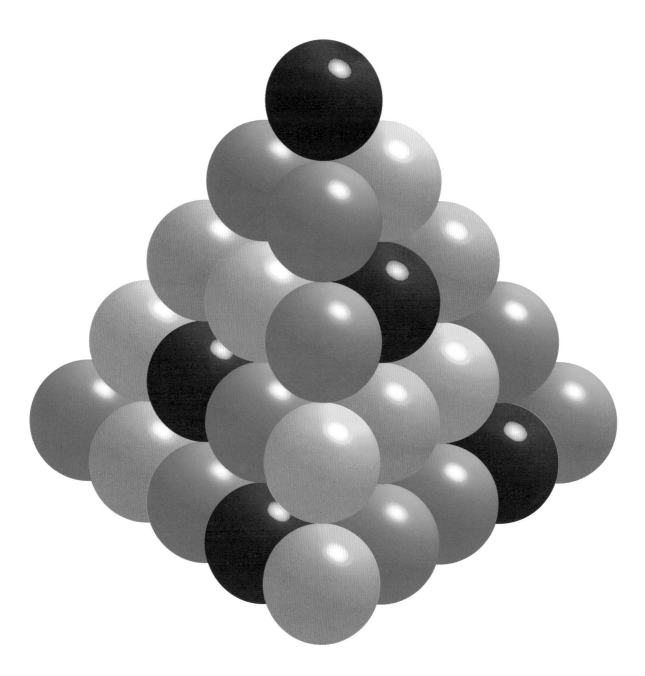

28

Oddball

A snooker club owner is offered five bushels of coloured balls, one each of red, blue, green, yellow and pink. He is told that balls of each colour weigh 3 oz – except for balls of one colour which weigh 3.1 oz. By using a springscale accurate to a tenth of an ounce, what is the minimum number of weighings he has to carry out to discover the odd ball?

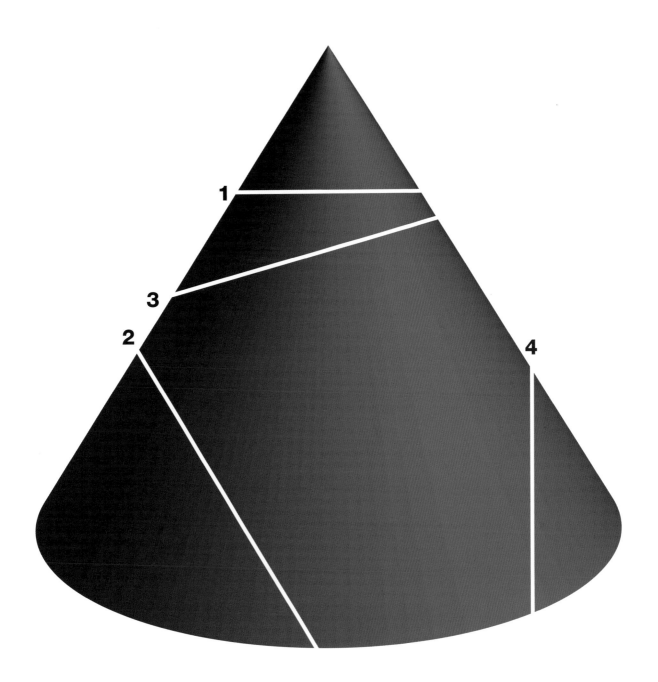

Plane Lines 29
If you cut a cone along the planes as
shown, what four curves would the
sections make?

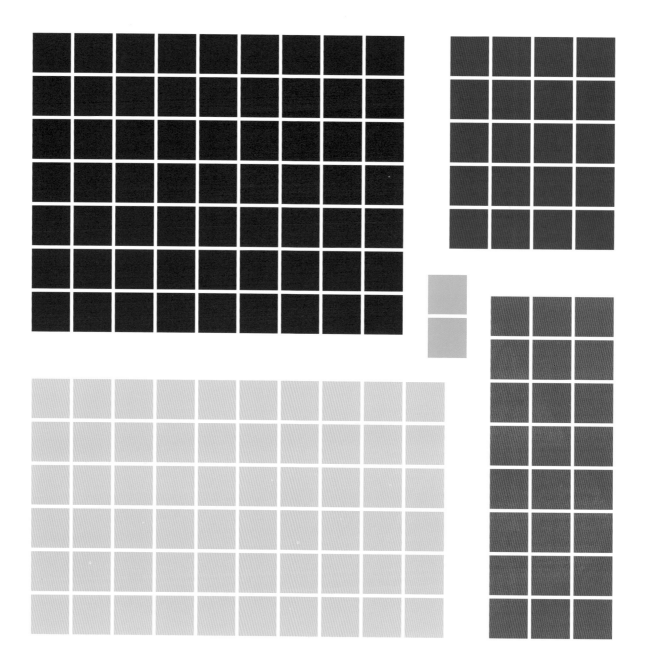

Rectangle Squares

Five rectangles are formed using the numbers 1 to 10 as their dimensions. How many squares can you make up from these rectangles? Can you make up a 13-by-13 square using all five rectangles?

Bishop's Move

Move the bishop around the chessboard so that it visits all the black squares in 17 moves.

1 ●●●

2 ●●●

3 ●●●

4 ●●●

5 ●●●

6 ●●●

7 ●●●

8 ●●●

9 ●●●

10 ●●●

11 ●●●

12 ●●●

13 ●●●

14 ●●●

15 ●●●

16 ●●●

17 ●●●

18 ●●●

The 18-point Line Game

On line 1 place a point anywhere you like. On line 2 place a second point exactly underneath the first point on line 1. Divide line 2 into two equal halves and place another point anywhere you like in the unoccupied half of the line. On line 3 place two points exactly underneath the two points on line 2. Divide the line into three equal parts and place another point in the unoccupied part of the line. Carry on like this through lines 4,5,6, etc, each time moving the existing points down to the next line, dividing up each line into equal parts one more than the previous line, and placing a new point in the unoccupied part of the line. Can you make it to line 18 without two points ever falling into the same part of the divided line?

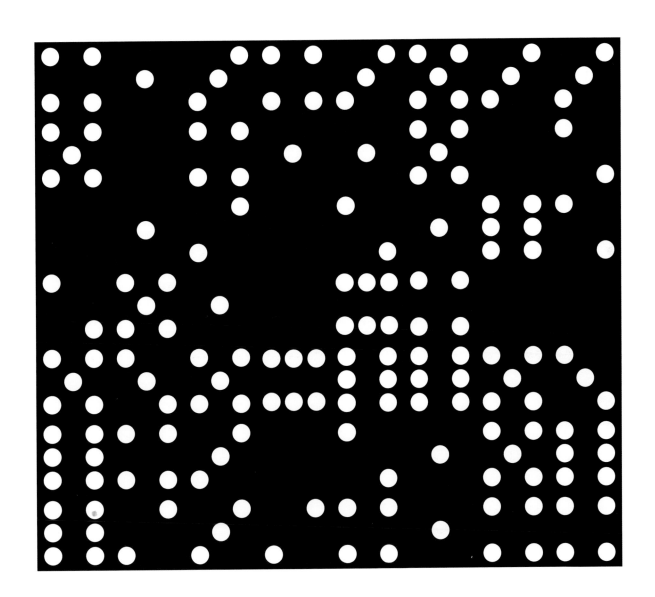

Invisible Dominoes

33

If this grid of dots were made out of a complete set of standard dominoes, how would the outlines of the individual pieces appear?

34

Reducing Squares

Divide a square into smaller squares so that none is the same size. For a long time, the record for the minimum number of squares was held at 24. Recently a 21-piece square has been achieved – now considered the fewest possible. If you manage to beat that you had better tell the world.

Circuit Board   **35**
Arrange the 19 hexagons so that you
create an unbroken closed line.

Adding Value
Distribute the remaining numbers
between 1 and 19 on the hexagon
so that the sum of each straight
line is 38.

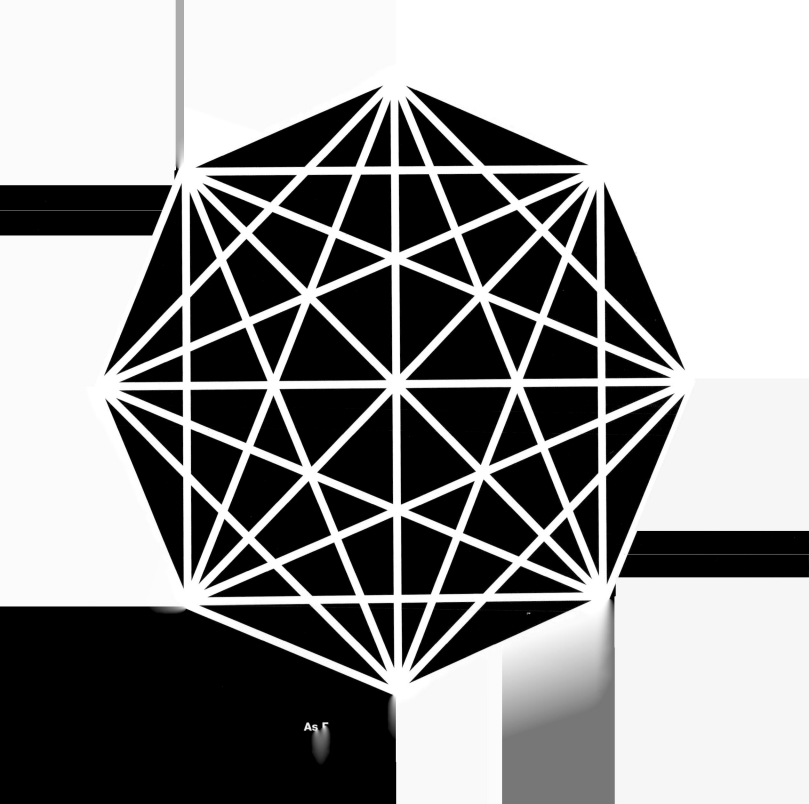
As E

Into Quarters
A 4-by-4 square may be divided
into quarters in five different ways.
All the divisions must be along the
grid lines.

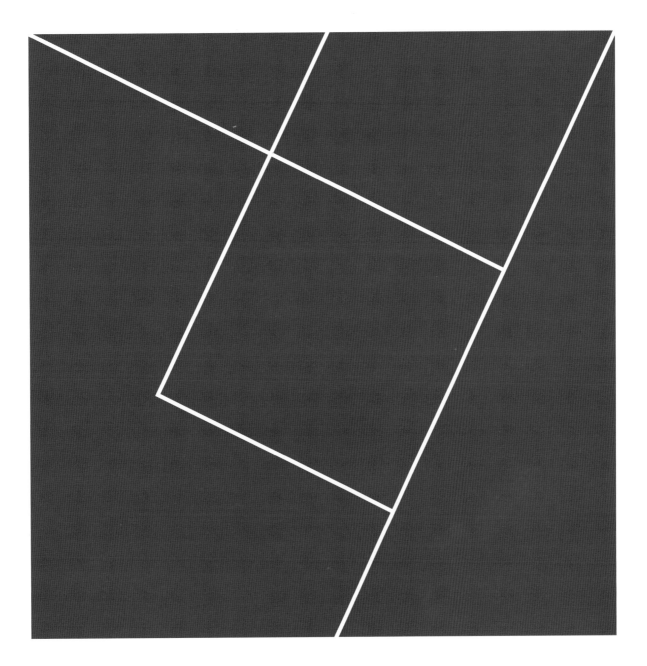

Five in All   **39**
Make a rectangle, triangle, Swiss
cross, parallelogram and rhombus
in succession so that each figure
contains the five shapes.

```
              1
            1   1
          1   2   1
        1   3   3   1
      1   4   6   4   1
    1   5  10  10   5   1
  1   6  15  20  15   6   1
1   7  21  35  35  21   7   1
1   8  28  56  70  56  28   8   1
1   9  36  84 126 126  84  36   9   1
1  10  45 120 210 252 210 120  45  10   1
```

Pascal's Numbers

The French mathematician Blaise Pascal originated this triangle made up from numbers that follow an entirely logical principle. By using the same logic can you discover what numbers would be needed to make up the extra row at the base of the triangle?

Internal Triangles
How many triangles can you find
in this pattern?

A Nine-letter Word
Can you spell out a nine-letter word by tracking from a letter to an adjacent letter going up, down, across or diagonally?

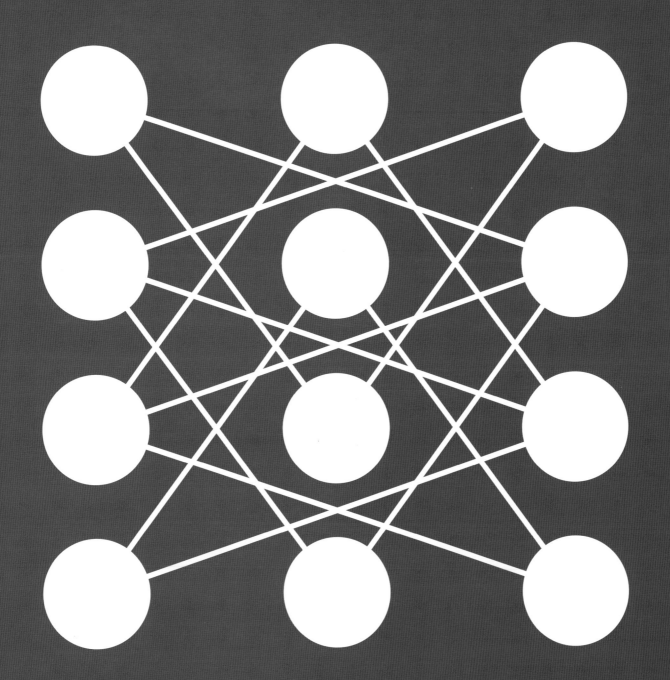

Along These Lines   **43**
Place 11 counters, one after the
other, on 11 of the 12 circles by first
placing each counter on an empty
circle and sliding it along one of the
lines to the circle where it ends up.

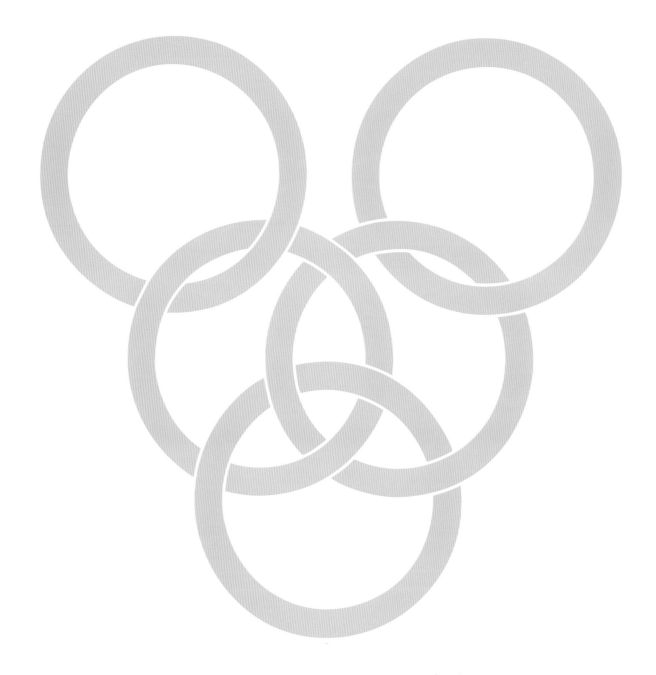

One Into Four
Which link has to be cut to separate
the chain into four pieces?

The Problem of Appollonius
How many different ways can you
draw a fourth circle so that it
touches all the original three circles?

This is known as the 'Problem of
Apollonius', one of the classic
problems solved in Greek antiquity.

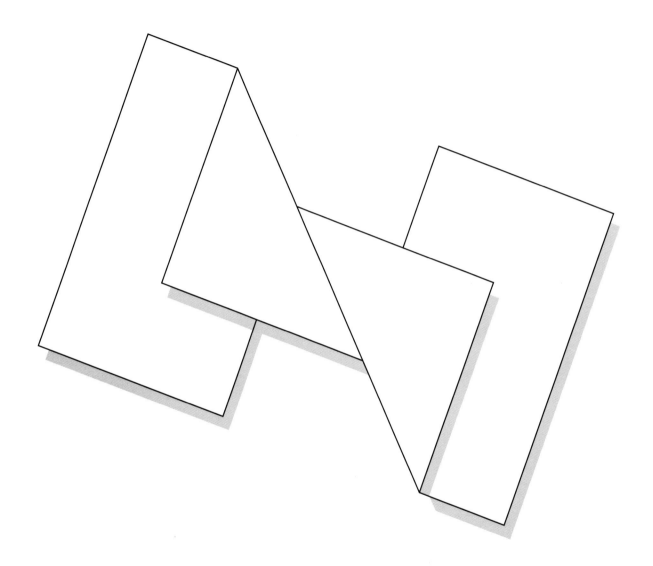

Paper Butterfly
You can create this butterfly
structure from a single piece
of paper simply by cutting and
folding (no gluing or fixing).

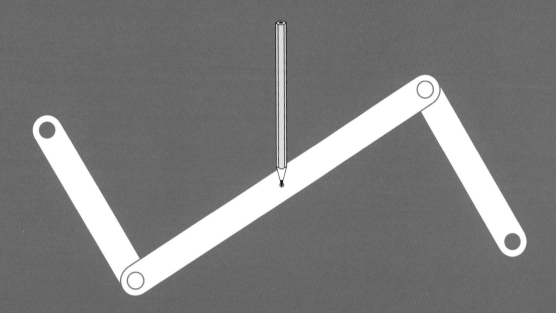

Just a Trace
Cut three strips of card and make
up the articulated figure laying flat on
paper. The two ends are fixed and
the two joints pinned so they can
move. Make a hole in the centre of
the middle member and place a
pencil through it onto the paper.
By moving the pencil in all directions
as far as it will go what path would
it trace?

100	99	98	97	96	95	94	93	92	91
65	64	63	62	61	60	59	58	57	90
66	37	36	35	34	33	32	31	56	89
67	38	17	16	15	14	13	30	55	88
68	39	18	5	4	3	12	29	54	87
69	40	19	6	1	2	11	28	53	86
70	41	20	7	8	9	10	27	52	85
71	42	21	22	23	24	25	26	51	84
72	43	44	45	46	47	48	49	50	83
73	74	75	76	77	78	79	80	81	82

Finding the Primes

Prime numbers are those which cannot be divided by any other number but themselves. Find all the prime numbers in the 100 number grid. How many are there? Note: number 1 is not considered a prime number by mathematicians.

Royal Visit

49

Move the queen around the chessboard so that she visits all the squares in 14 moves.

BAYSWATER · J. W. CARPENTER L.ᵗᵈ · 180 – 184 QUEEN'S Rᵈ

50

Why Round?
Why are manhole covers round?
Can you find at least three good
reasons?

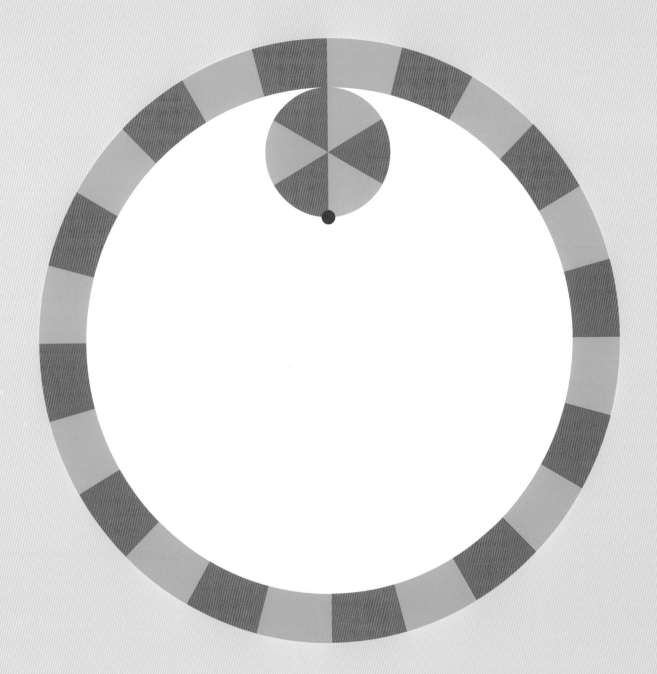

Little Wheel

51

If the small wheel runs round
the inside of the big wheel, draw
freehand the curves that would be
traced by the point shown on the
small wheel as it moves.

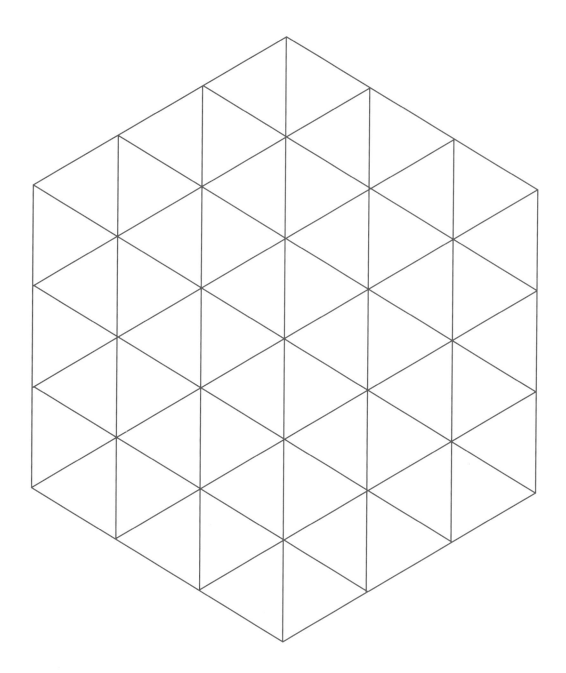

Net Amount
How many fish can the fishing net hold if the fish remain whole and do not overlap?

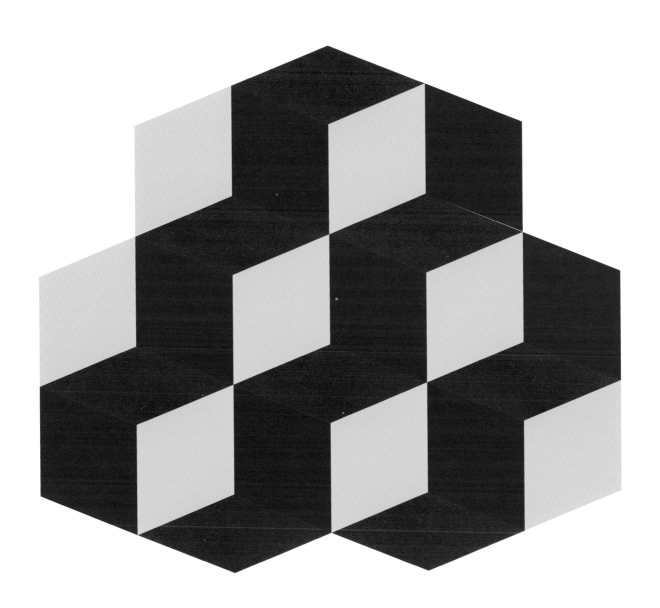

Mystery Cubes
Count the number of cubes. Are you
sure? Turn the page upside down
and count them again.

53

54

Five Makes Ten
This five-pointed star (or pentagram) is made up from 17 parts. How would you cut them out and rearrange them to form four identical ten-sided figures (or decagons)?

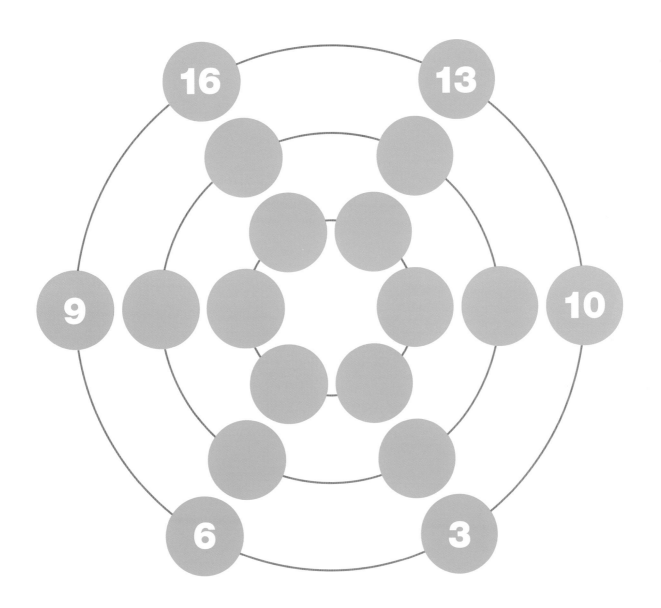

Opposite Numbers 55
Arrange the numbers 1 to 18 on
the diameters in pairs so that the
sum of the two numbers in the
corresponding symmetrical
positions all add up to 19.

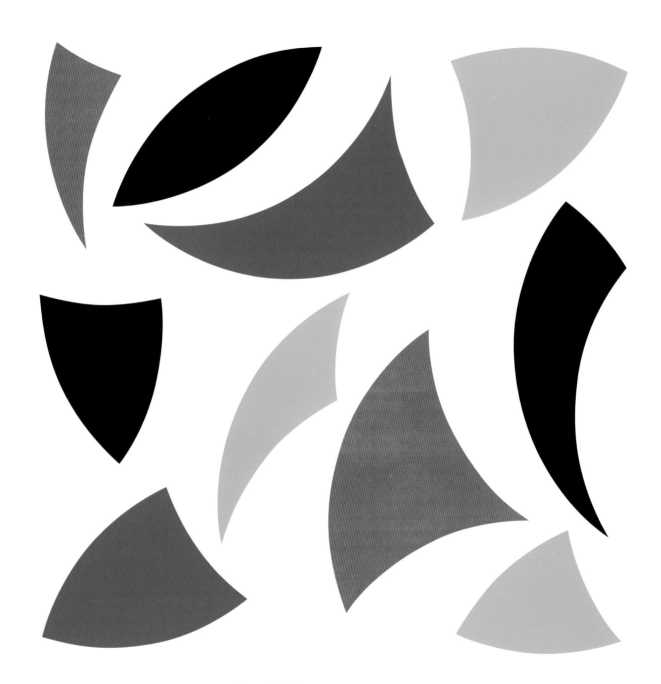

Curved Ball

These ten pieces with their curved sides are parts of a perfect circle. Photocopy the page and cut out the pieces. Then see how long it takes you to recreate the circle - not so easy as it might seem. The beauty of the construction is that all the curves are of the same radius, which is also the radius of the circle itself.

Meeting Points

57

Within the square, can you make five lines intersect at ten different points? Do you reckon that ten is the greatest number of points at which five lines can intersect?

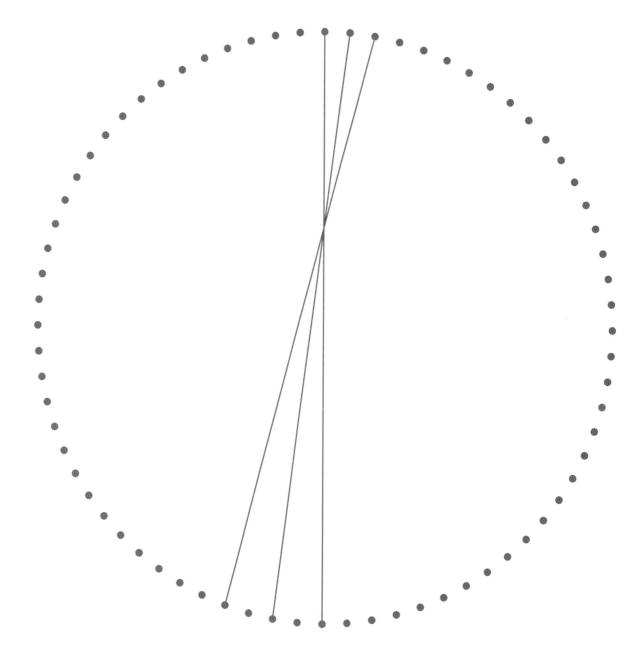

Valentine's Circle
By connecting the points in the big
circle in the same way as the first
three lines have been drawn, what
shape will you end up with?

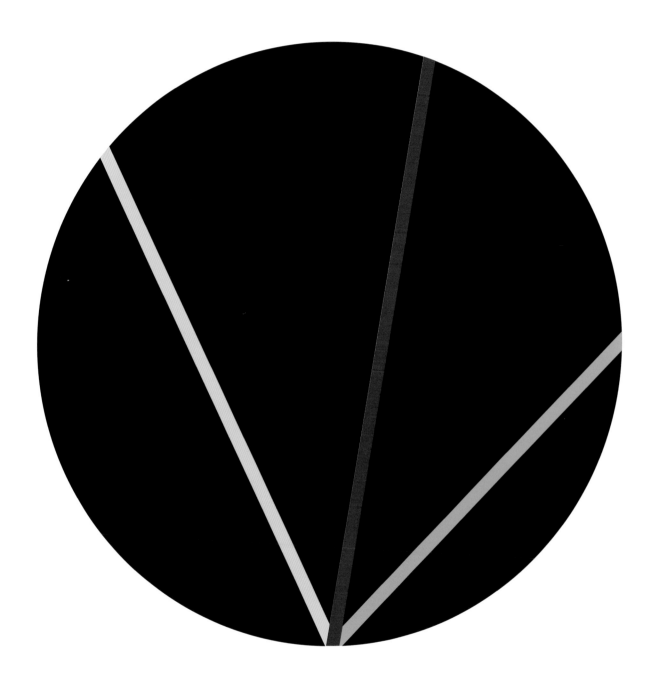

Mystery Wheel 59
Imagine the wheel cut out and balanced on the point of a pencil and given a spin. Guess what will happen to the 3 coloured lines when the wheel revolves?

Three's Company
You want to invite nine friends to dinner, three at a time over twelve days. How would you arrange the invitations so that pairs of friends only meet each other once?

NEW
DOOR

One Out of Two
There's one word you can make out
of the letters in the two words.

61

Inside Number
Using the lines of the grid, find the
fewest number of triangles that can
fit into the large triangle figure. Some
of the component triangles can be
the same size.

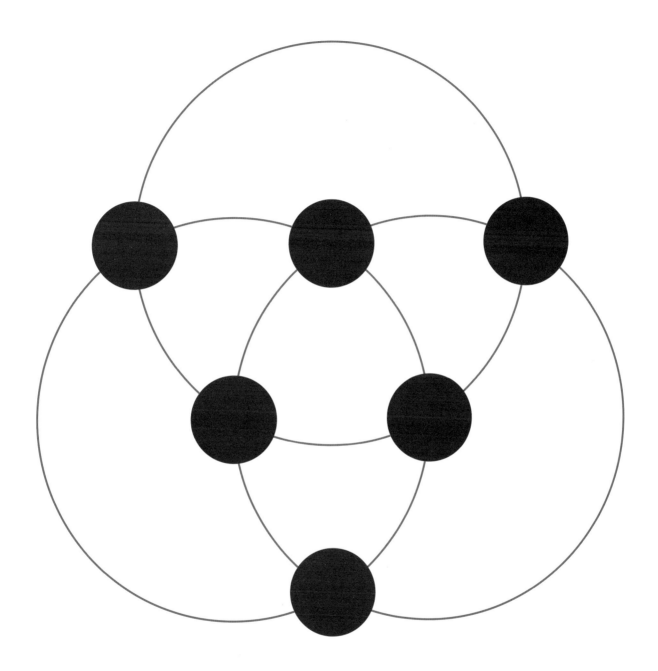

Same Way Round 63
Distribute the numbers 1 to 6 on
the intersections of three circles so
that the sum on any given circle is
equal to the sum of the numbers on
any other.

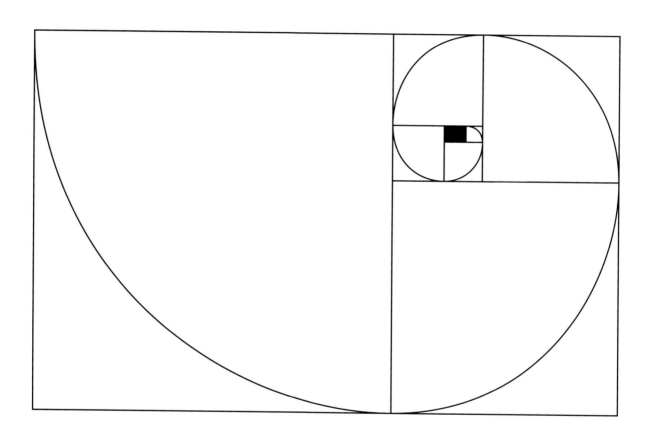

The Divine Proportion
Can you continue this number
sequence, known as the
Fibonnacci Series?

Any Which Way   **65**
Distribute the numbers 1 to 16 in the
square gird so that in any row or any
column and along either diagonal
they always add up to 34.

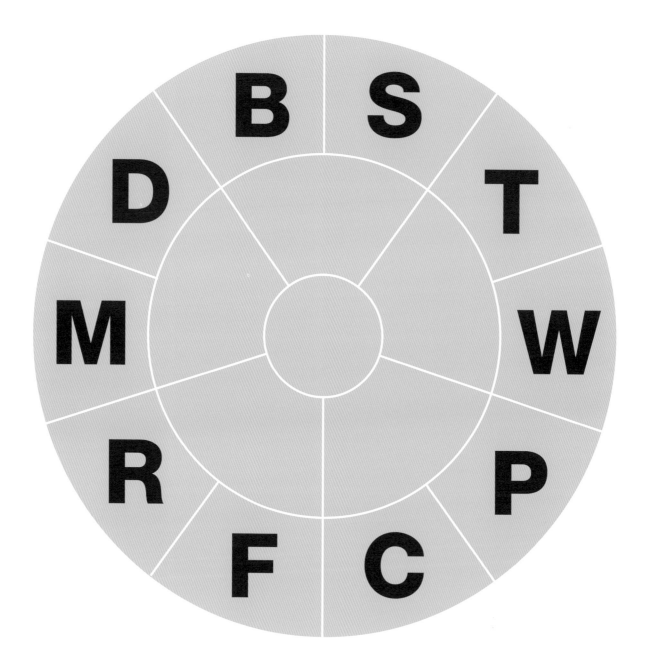

66

Target Words
Fill in the blank spaces to make ten three-letter words reading inward. The centre letter is a consonant and the inner ring is made up with five different vowels.

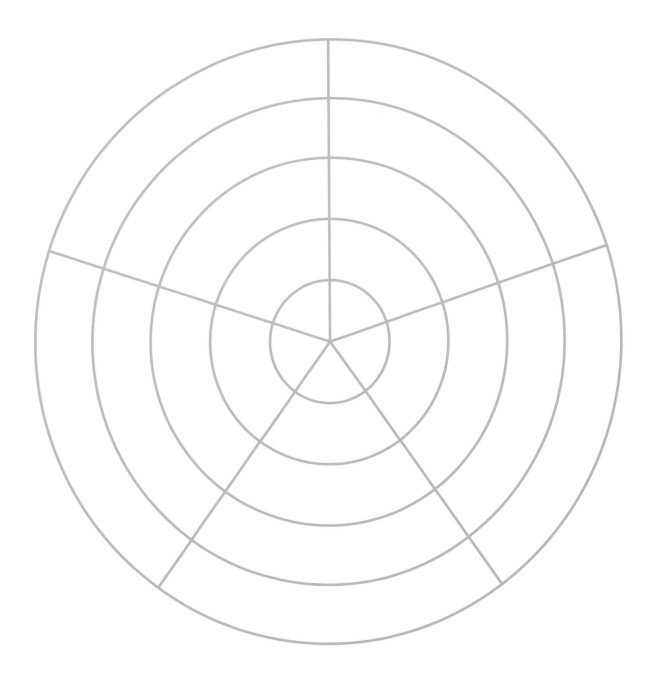

A Piece of Cake

A cake is divided into five equal slices and also divided into the same number of concentric circles. Using five different colours, fill in the segments of the cake so that the same colours never touch, even across the corner points.

Folding Stamps
In how many different ways can you fold the strip of four stamps along their joined perforated sides?

Strip Tease

These nine different strips of colours can be arranged in a 5-by-5 grid so that there are five different colours in every row and every column.

T Junctions
The three T shapes can be fitted together without overlapping into the square grid so that no colours appear more than once in any row or any column.

Mirror Letters

Find all letters of the alphabet that are symmetrical, ie those that can be divided either vertically or horizontally into mirror-image halves. Some letters may have more than one line of symmetry. For instance, half of a capital A divided vertically would appear as the complete letter in a mirror. The same applies to a capital E divided horizontally.

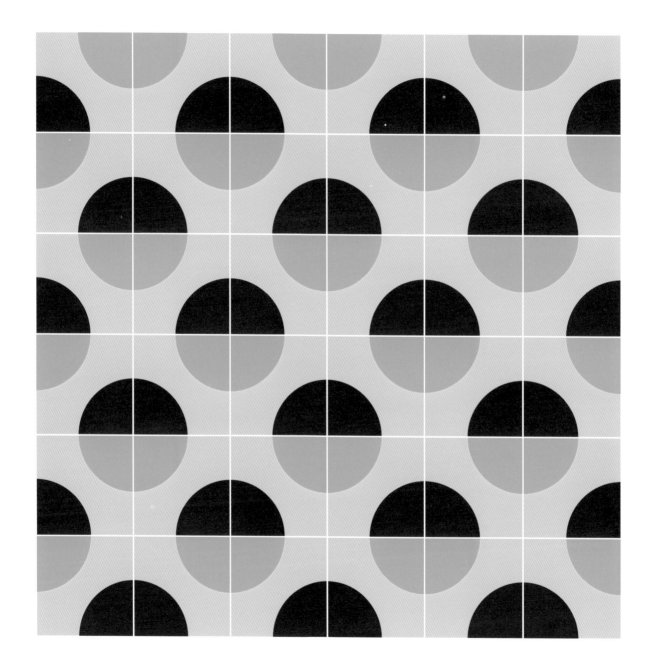

72

Baker's Dozen
There are 36 square tiles, each with a coloured quarter circle on its two opposing corners, making up a pattern with twelve complete circles.

Using the same tiles, can you make up a square configuration with a thirteenth complete circle?

Queens at Peace

The chess queen can move up and down, across and diagonally on a chessboard. Place three white queens and four black queens on a 6-by-6 board so that no queen is attacked by a queen of the opposing colour.

Halving Shapes
Can you divide this shape exactly in
two parts by a single line (straight,
broken or curved). The halves must
be the same shape and size.

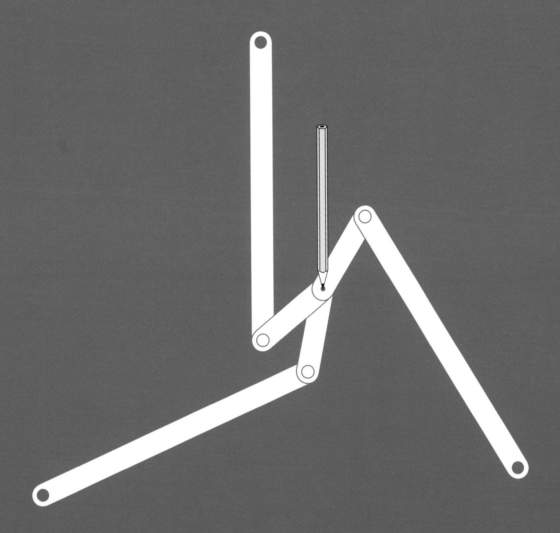

Crank Case

Cut six strips of card, three long and three short as shown, and make up the articulated figure laying flat on paper. The three end points are fixed and the four centre joints are pinned so they can move. Make a hole at the centre and place a pencil through it. By moving the pencil in all directions as far as it will go what path would it trace?

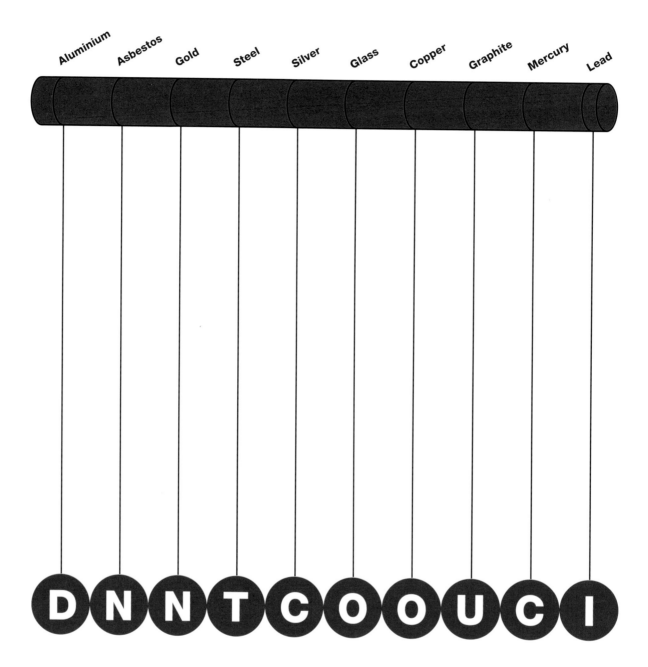

Aluminium　Asbestos　Gold　Steel　Silver　Glass　Copper　Graphite　Mercury　Lead

D N N T C O O U C I

Melt Down

Each wire hanging from a heating element is made of a different material. At the end of each wire is a disc joined on by wax. The wax will melt at different times, depending on the rate the heat is transferred down each material. Thus the letters will drop off their wires in a definite sequence. Can you tell what the sequence is and thus what word the letters will make in that sequence?

723
7x2x3=42
4x2=8

Persistence Puzzles
To illustrate what a 'number of persistence' is, take as an example the number 723. Multiply the individual digits together: 7 x 2 x 3 = 42. Repeat the process with the answer 42: 4 x 2 = 8. That's 2 stages - you can't go further than that. So 2 is the number of persistence for the number 723. What is the smallest number of persistence (this is easy!). What are the smallest numbers that lead to the numbers of persistence 2,3,4 and 5? Can you tell whether every starting number leads to a single digit number in the end? Or can the process go on forever (ie the number of persistence is infinity)?

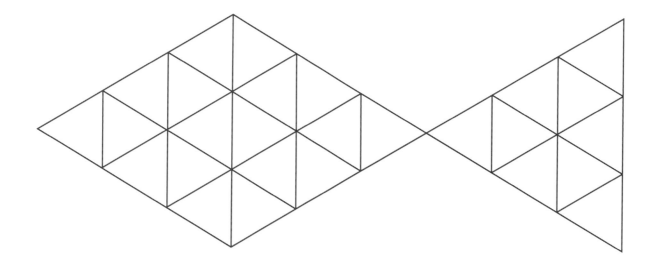

78

Big Fish Eats Little Fish
The large fish eats as many as
possible of the small fish. If the
small fish remain whole, how
many can the large fish fit inside
without overlapping?

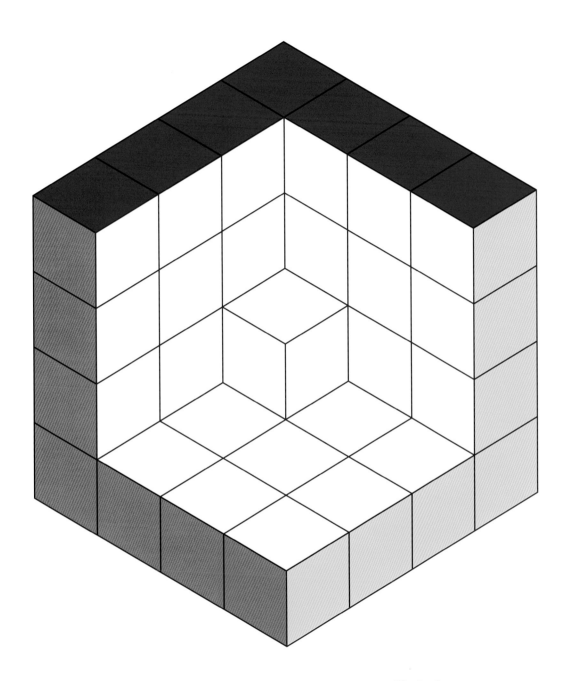

Blocks Away 79
How many individual cube building
blocks would be needed to complete
the large cube structure? And what
would the colours of the missing
cube blocks be?

Ways of Getting Through
By twisting and turning the
nine shapes how many ways
in all can you fit each into its
corresponding hole?

Close Encounters

Can you tell what figures will result
if you close this arrangement of
shapes at the hinges, first clockwise
and then anti-clockwise?

Square of Triangles
Take 20 right-angle triangles as shown and make one square using all of them. If you find this tricky, an easier problem is to make a square using 16 of the triangles.

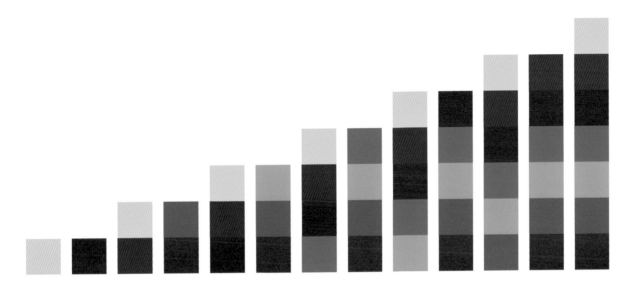

Colour Bars

Thirteen strips made up of coloured blocks can be arranged in a 7-by-7 square so that each horizontal row is a single colour. Rearrange the strips so that no colour appears more than once in any horizontal or vertical row. Rearrange them again so that no colour appears more than once in the diagonals.

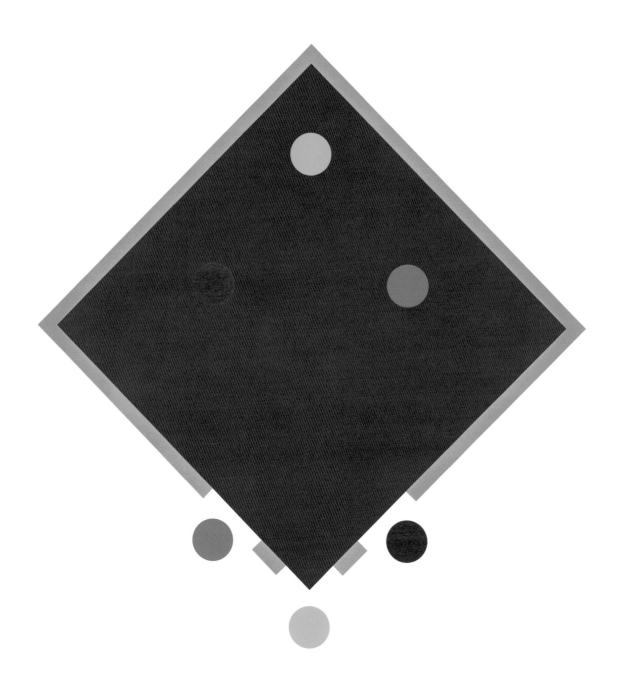

Private Lines
Draw three lines from the outside
balls to their corresponding colours
inside so that they do not cross.

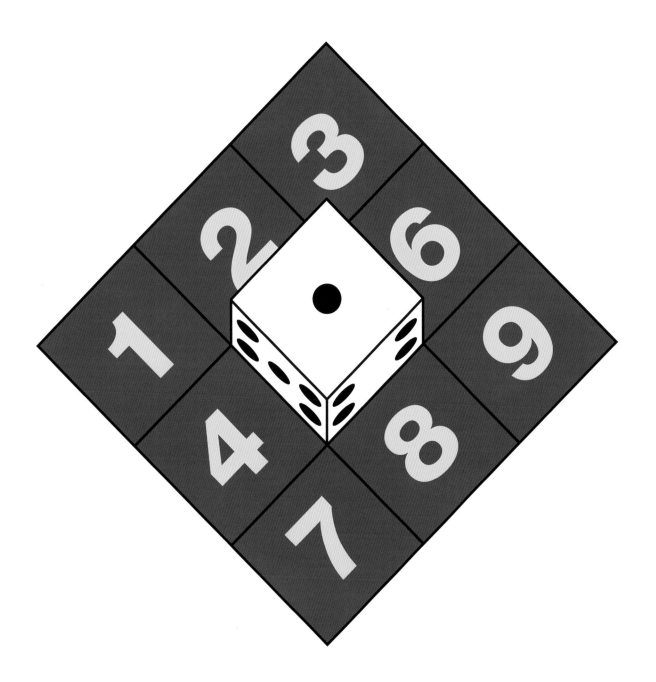

Six on Seven

From the original position in the square, roll the dice one face at a time six times so that it ends up on square 7 with its six face on top.

Can you achieve this in a smaller number of moves, always rolling the dice one face at a time?

Sixteen by Six
Can you draw a continuous
line which has no more than six
straight parts and passes through
all 16 points?

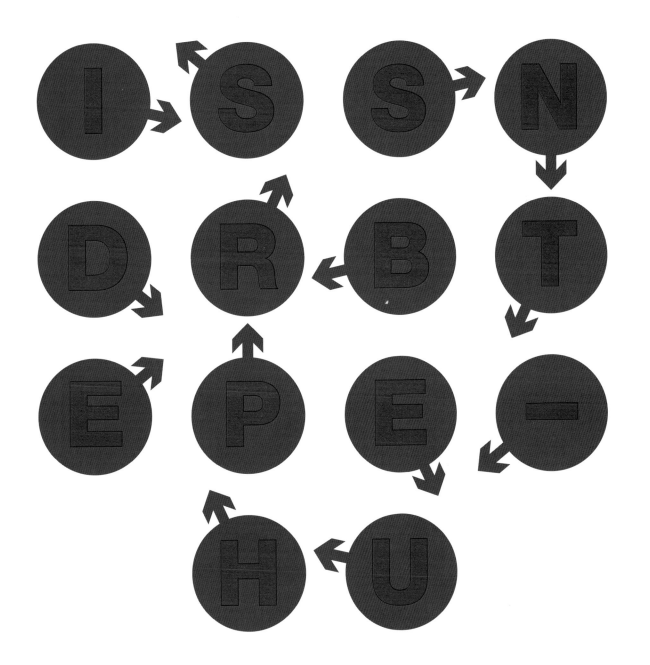

Big Chief Arrowpoints

By moving the letters into the order indicated by the arrows you can decipher the name of a well-known leader.

87

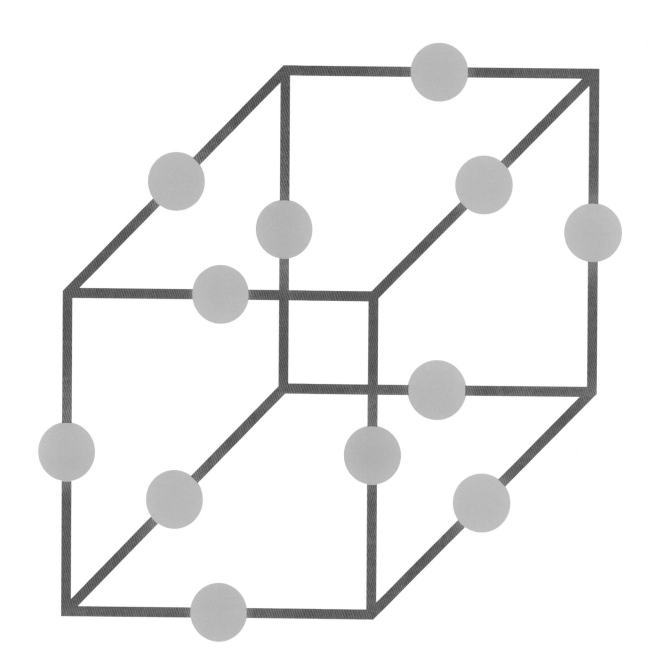

It All Adds Up
Distribute the numbers 1 to 12 on
the edges of the cube so that the
sums of the four edges around one
face all equal 26.

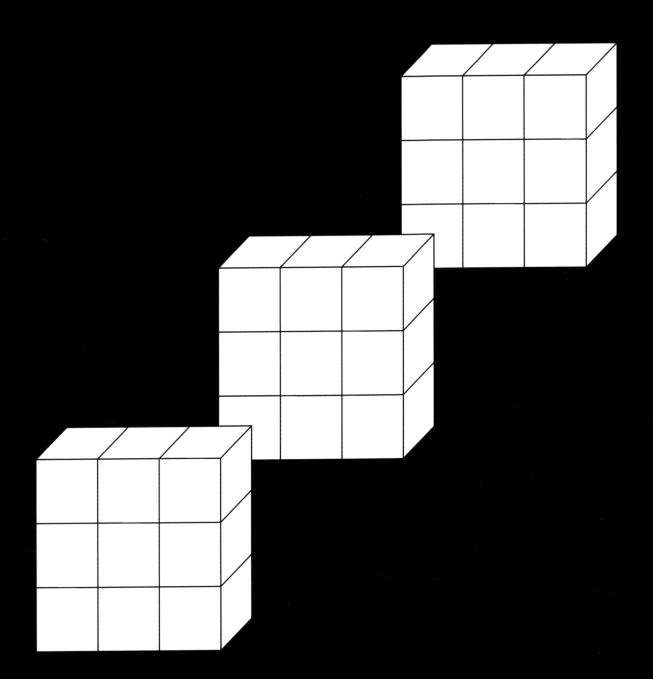

Colour Coding

A 3-by-3 cube is divided into 27 smaller cubes. Using three colours fill in each of the smaller cubes so that each colour appears nine times and all the vertical columns and horizontal rows contain all three colours.

89

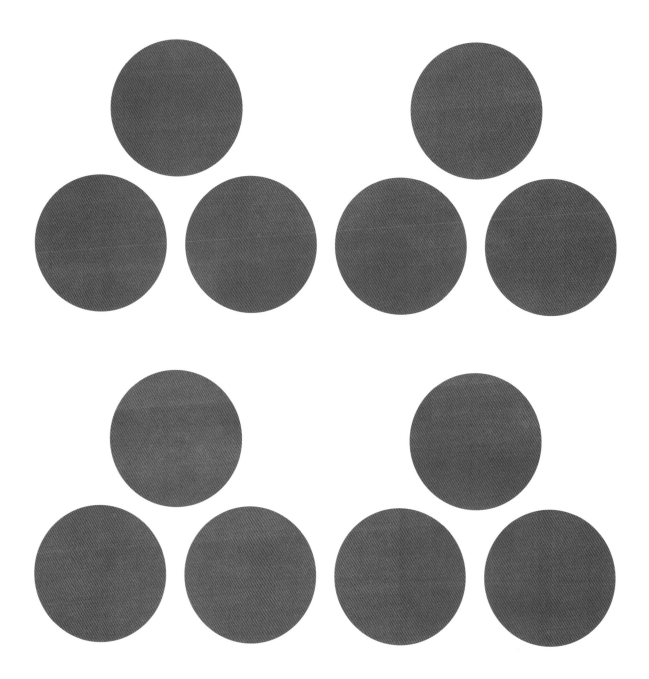

90

Spot Numbers
Distribute the numbers 1 to 6 twice on the four groups of circles so that every number appears only on two groups and every two groups has one number in common.

123456789=100

Nine to Make a Hundred
By inserting either plus or minus
signs in the 1-to-9 sequence, make
it total 100. (You can run together
two of the digits into one number in
the sequence).

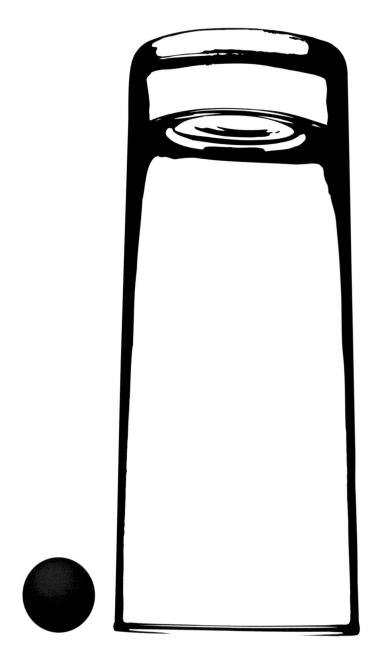

92

The Magic Marble
Can you lift a marble off a table
without touching it and only
using a glass?

Strings Unattached 93
Find how many different pieces
of string there are in this tangle.

94

Three's a Crowd
Place 14 counters on a 7-by-7 board of squares so that there are no three counters in a row - horizontally, vertically or diagonally.

Swinging Compass

95

Place the compass point in each of
the squares of a 4-by-4 grid so that
north, south, east and west never
appear more than once in any row
or any column.

96

Apple Shake

If you fill a bowl with apples of different sizes and shake it for a while, will the bigger and heavier apples end up at the bottom or lay on the top?

Two Equal Halves 97
This shape can be divided in half by
a single line so that the two halves
are exactly the same shape and size
as each other. The line may be
straight, angled or curved.

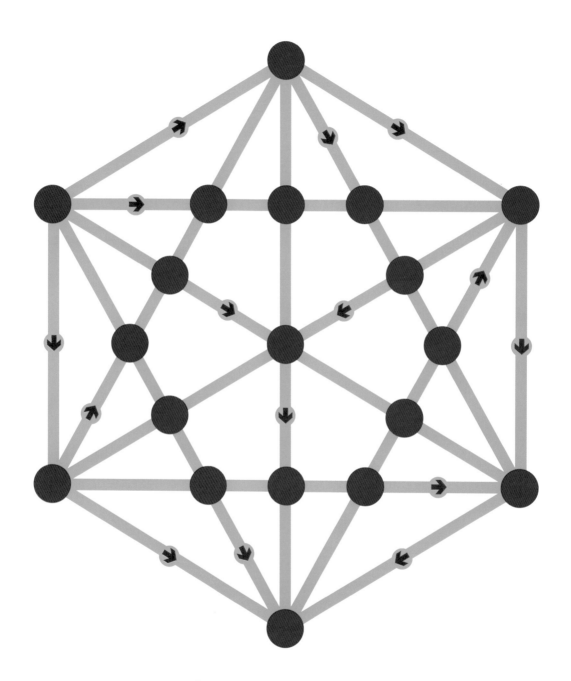

One-touch Passing
Mark any circle on the board as 'Point 1'. Start here and draw a continuous line from point to adjacent point only in the direction of the arrows. You must touch each point only once and visit all 19 points. It's difficult – if you can't manage it, see what your best result will be.

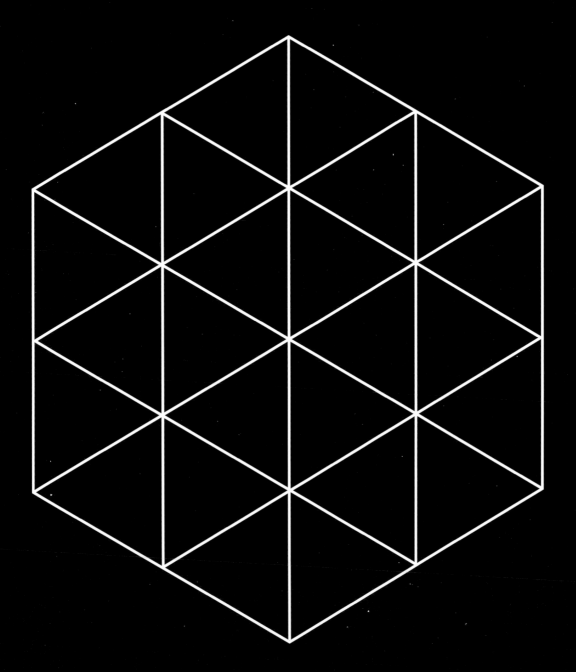

Colour Fit
See how many colour variations of the triangle can you achieve by filling in the three segments using combinations of four colours.

Now fit the resulting different coloured triangles into the hexagon figure so that the touching edges are all the same colour.

100

Keep on Adding

A circle is drawn with a radius of 1 unit. Around it is drawn an equilateral triangle. Another circle is drawn through the points of the triangle and around that circle is drawn a square.

Through the corners of the square another circle is drawn and around that circle is drawn a five-sided figure. If you were to carry on like this, adding one more side to each

polygon and increasing the sizes of circle to suit, how big would the circle eventually become in relation to its original radius? The answer is not infinity.

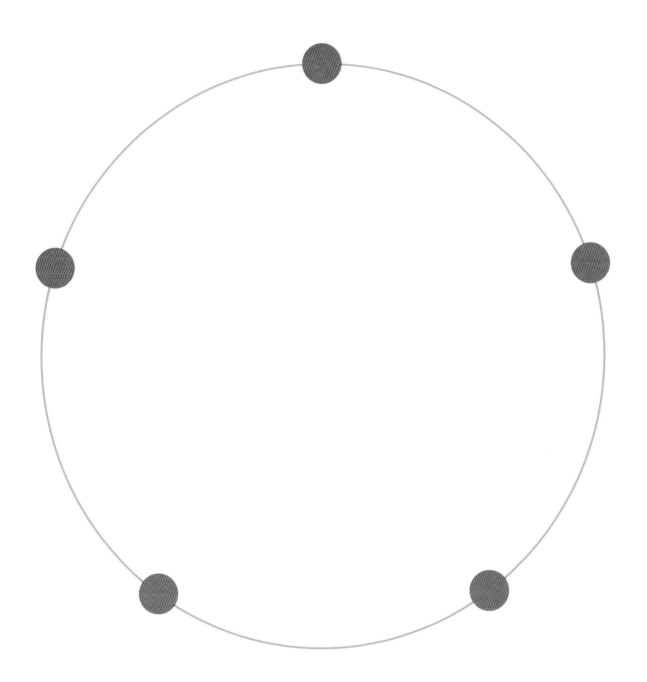

Figure Connections

Five points are arranged at equal distances on the circumference of a circle. Draw all the different polygons that can be made by connecting all five points.

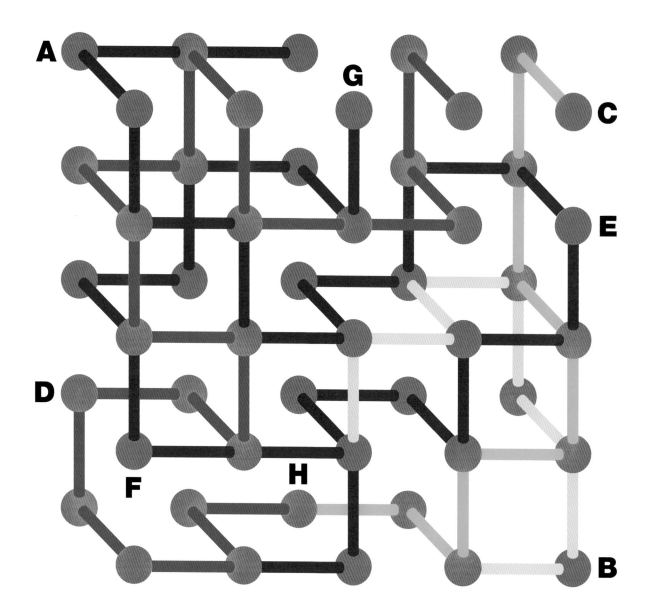

Subway Planner
Find the shortest routes between the stations A and B, C and D, E and F, and G and H on the subway network. Count each station you pass – including the start – as one move and any station where you change lines as two moves.

Figure Figures

How many triangles of different sizes can you find in the square pattern?

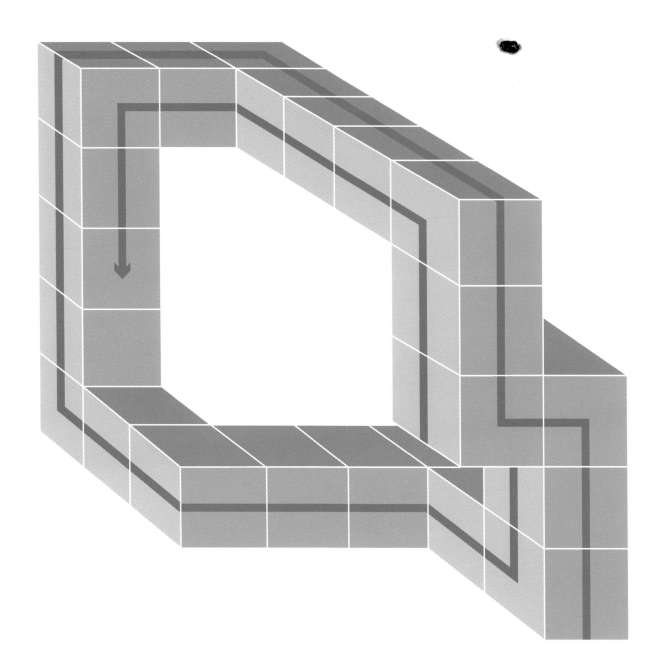

Smaller Than That

The cube ring is made up of 22 individual cube blocks. It has one face and one edge. Make a similar structure still forming a closed ring with one face and one edge, but with the fewest number of cube blocks possible.

Number Cascade

Arrange the numbers 1 to 16 in the empty squares so that no square has a higher value either next to it on the right, or immediately below it.

13	5	2	16	÷	+	−
10	15	3	2	+	÷	X
4	7	14	11	=	=	+
6	8	9	12	=	X	=

All the Right Answers
Make a photocopy of this page
and cut out the seven vertical strips.
Rearrange the strips to make four
mathematical equations with
correct answers.

4 5 3 5 6 2 4 8

Countdown
What would the final number in this sequence be?

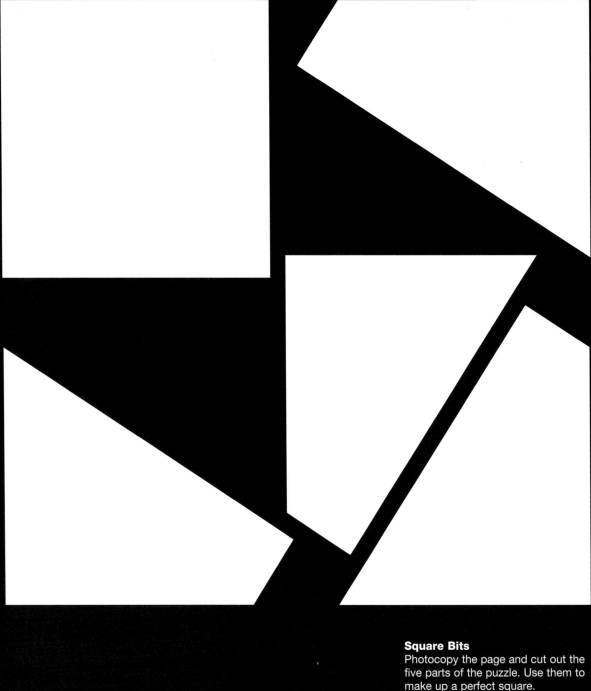

Square Bits
Photocopy the page and cut out the
five parts of the puzzle. Use them to
make up a perfect square.

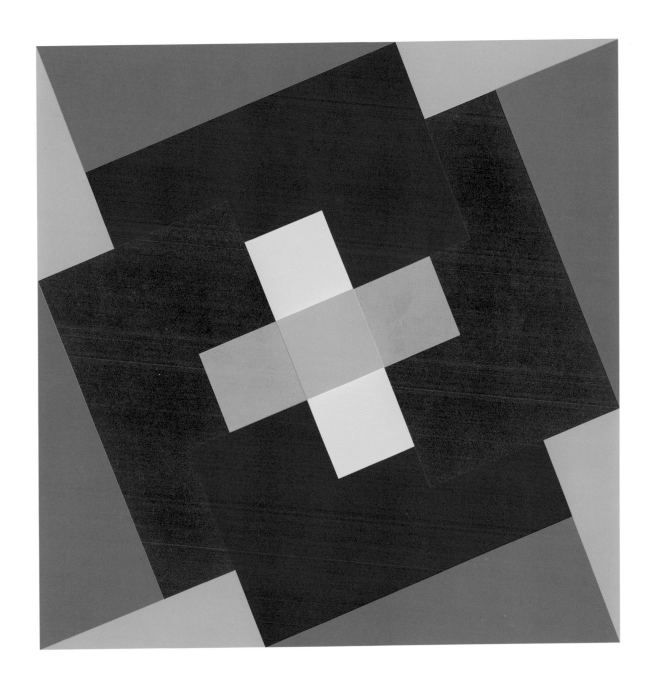

Impossible Squares

Rearrange the puzzle pieces in the square shown removing the small green square, as shown. The mystery is that, although you have subtracted the green square, the whole outer square appears to have remained the same size. But that's impossible.

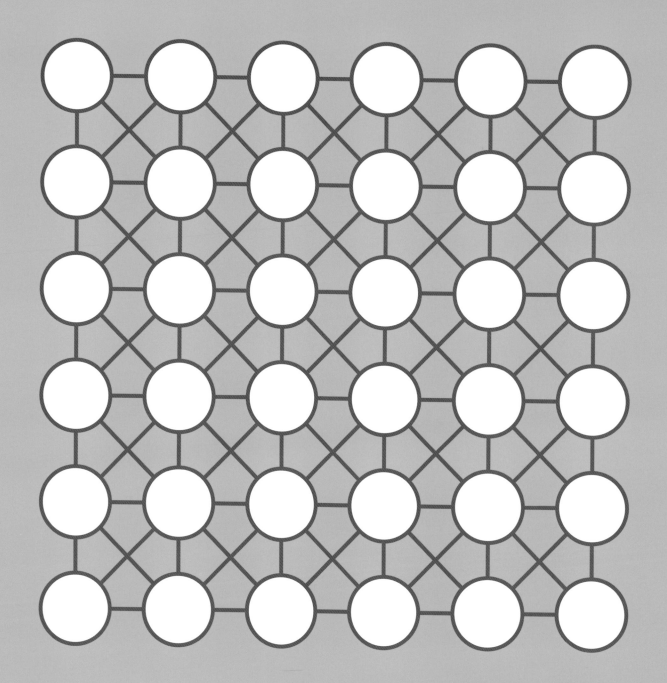

Unequal Contest
Place six points on a 6-by-6 grid so that all the distances between the points are different.

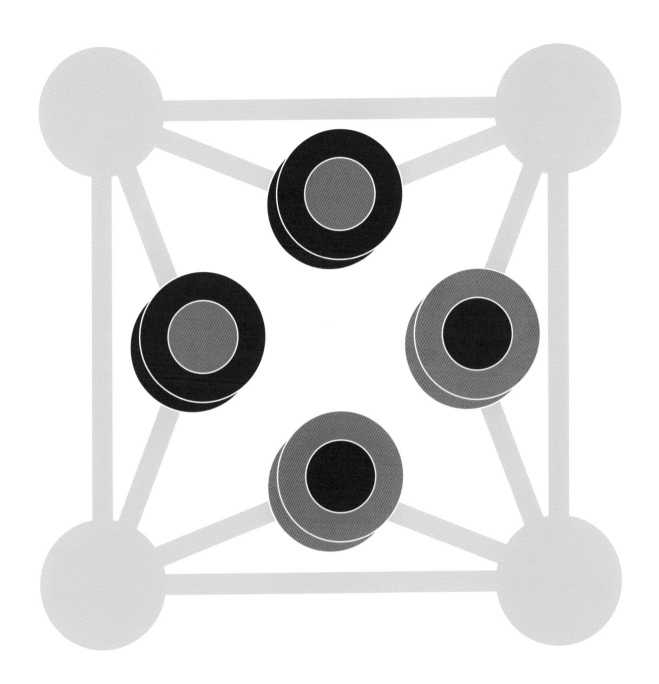

Reverse Moves

Two orange pieces and two purple pieces are placed on a board, as shown. By moving the pieces alternately – first an orange piece, then a purple piece and so on – slide them along the lines from one circle to another so that they end up in the reverse positions. How many moves do you have to make to achieve the switch?

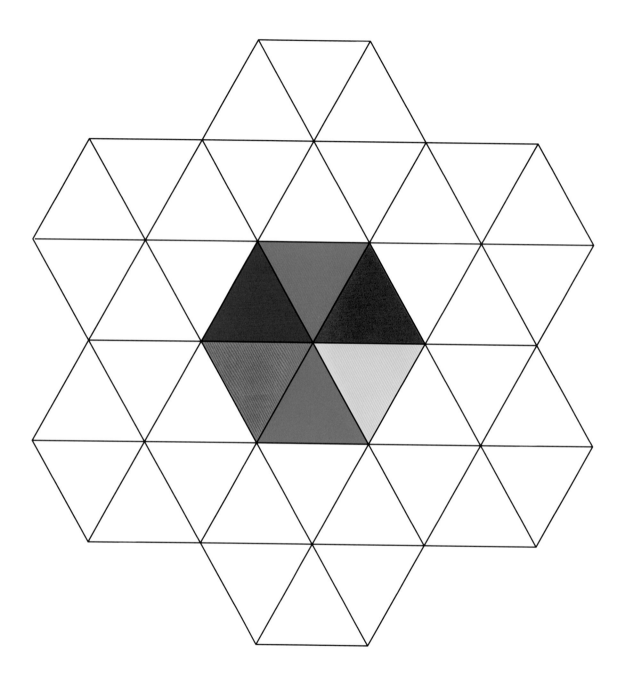

Colour-Comb
Place the six colours arranged in hexagons as shown into the honeycomb figure above so that all the touching edges are in matching colours.

Star Generation   113
The elements of the large star
can be arranged to make three
smaller replicas.

114

Different Directions
Choose an arrow in each box of the grid so that no two arrows are pointing in the same direction in any row or any column.

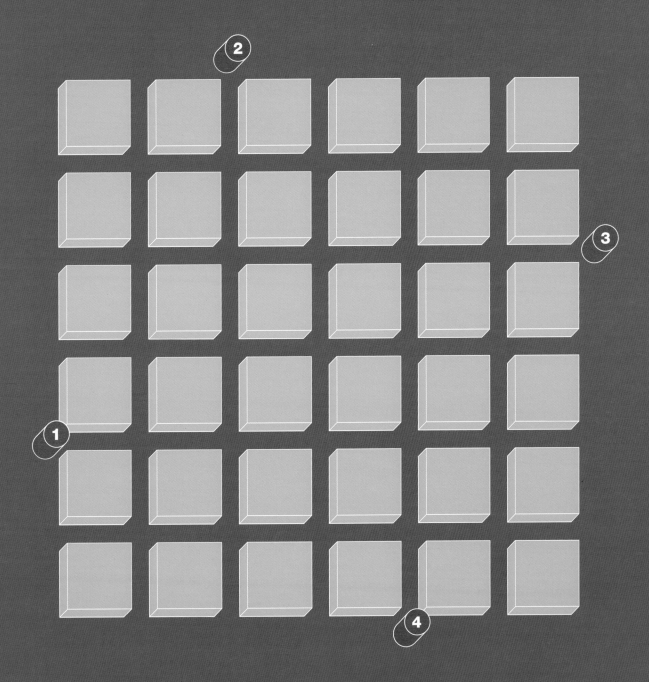

Fair Taxi

In a city with a grid street pattern, a taxicab driver is called out to visit three places and then return to base. The driver works out the shortest route starting from 1 and visiting in succession 2, 3, 4 and back to 1 again. How does he do it, and are there any other routes that he could have taken that are equally short?

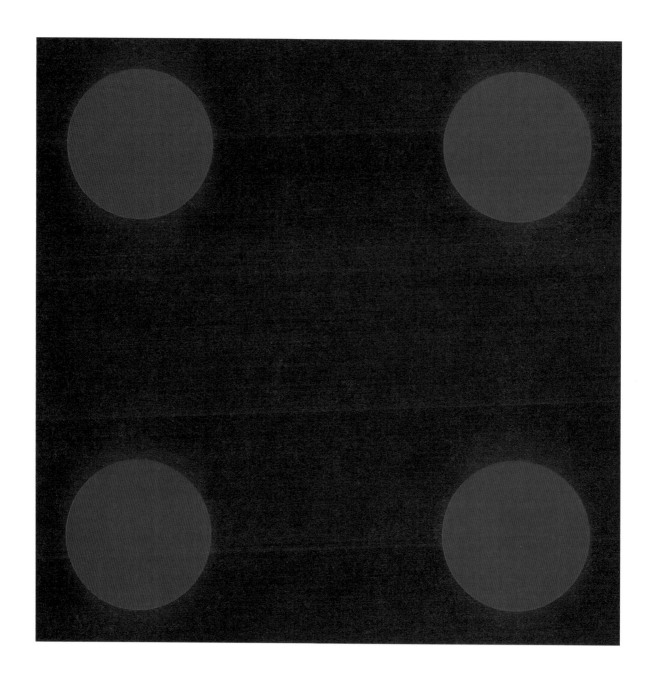

Budget Highways

Four towns happen to be situated at the four points of a square. Draw out a road system so that all the towns are interconnected and the total length of the road is as short as possible. The answer by the way is not an X configuration.

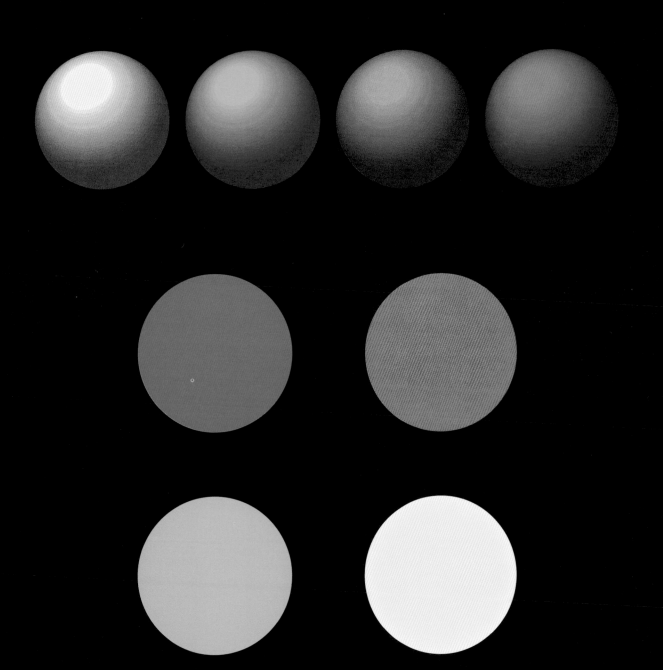

Exclusive Trails   117
Trace the paths of the spheres so
that they end up in their same colour
holes without their paths crossing.

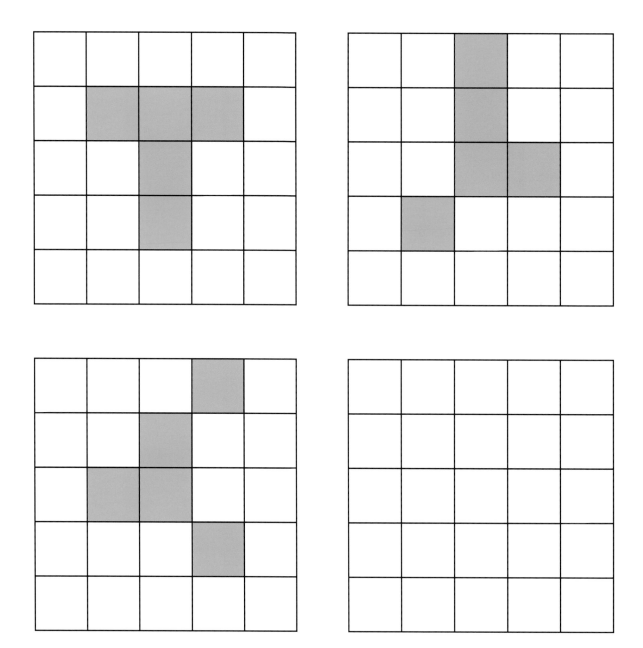

Four Follows Three

The three patterns in the square grid follow a logical sequence. Can you complete the sequence by working out what the pattern in the fourth square should be?

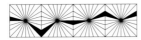

Colour Connections

Each side of these four squares is made up of six colours from the radial segments. By making different arrangements of the four squares stacked together in a line, make all the colours except for one form a continuous zig-zag. What is the odd colour out?

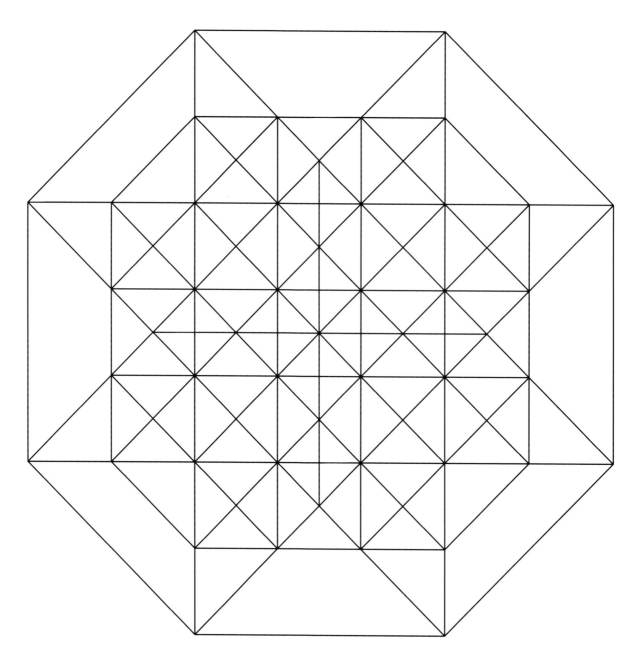

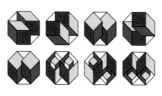

Cubism
Can you create these eight cube figures by tracing lines from the central pattern?

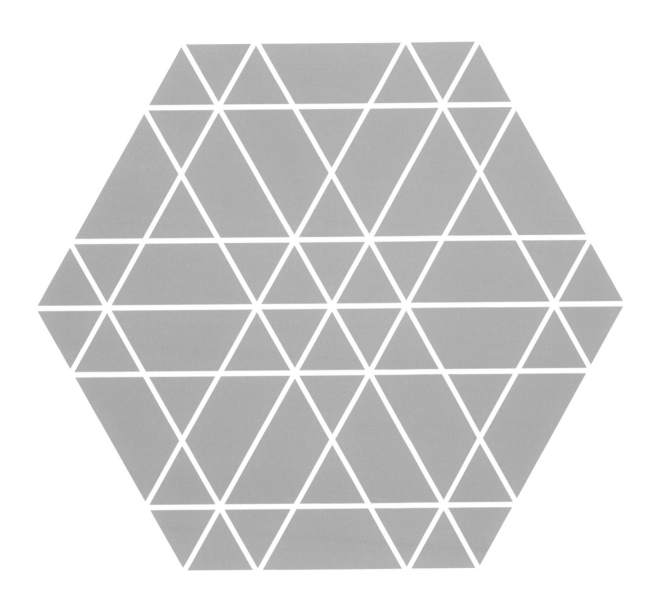

Inside Six Sides   **121**
How many regular hexagons can you
find inside the large hexagon?

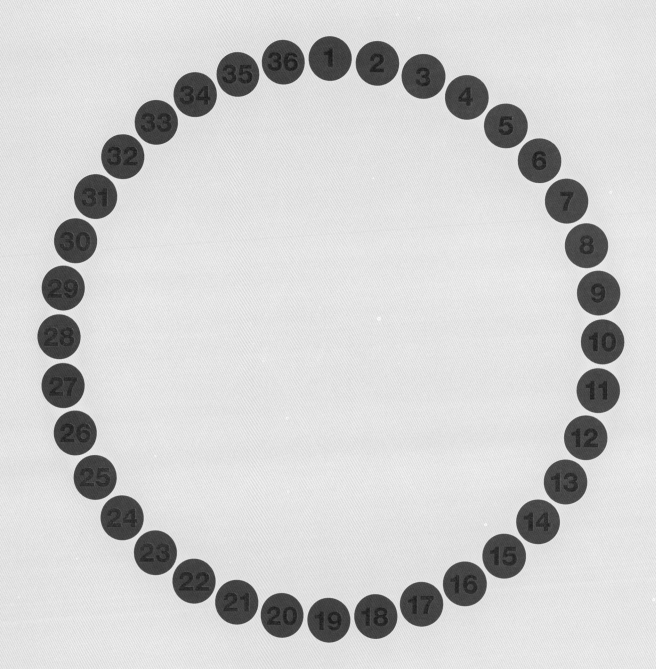

The First Half Dozen
Imagine 36 people in a circle. Counting from number 1, every tenth person is removed (so number 10 is the first to go). If you were to continue in this way, pick which six numbers would be the first to be eliminated.

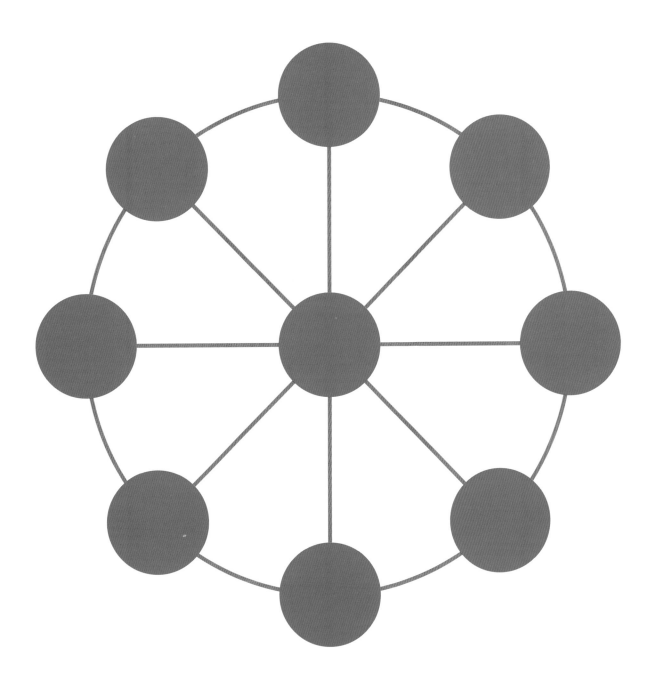

Bespoke Solution   **123**
Distribute the numbers 1 to 9 so
that the lines across the wheel all
add up to 15.

124

With Touches of Colour
Twenty hexagons are divided into
three colours each, using six colours
in all. Arrange the hexagons so that
all the touching sides are in a
matching colour.

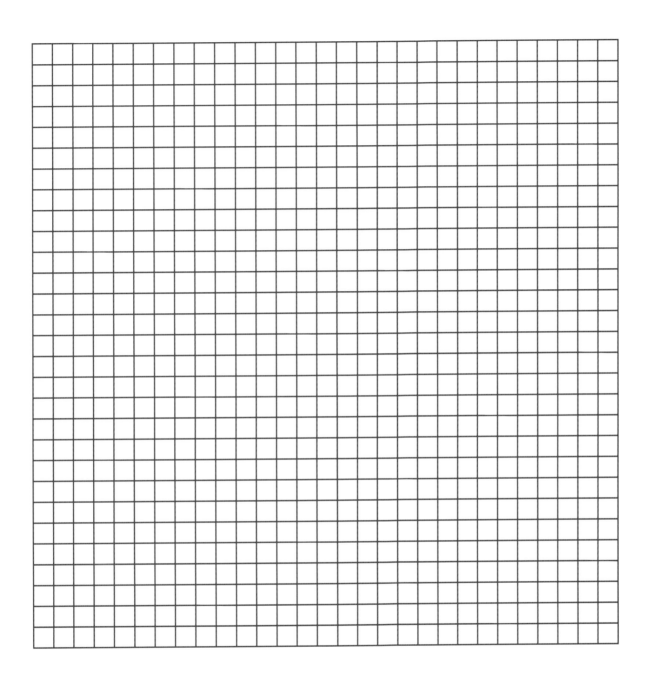

Set Squares

Start by filling in the single square at the centre with a colour. Now add a set of squares in a different colour around the original square, so that each of the new squares never touches more than one side of the original square. Following this rule add further sets of squares, each set in a different colour until the whole grid is filled. Tabulate the number of squares in each set.

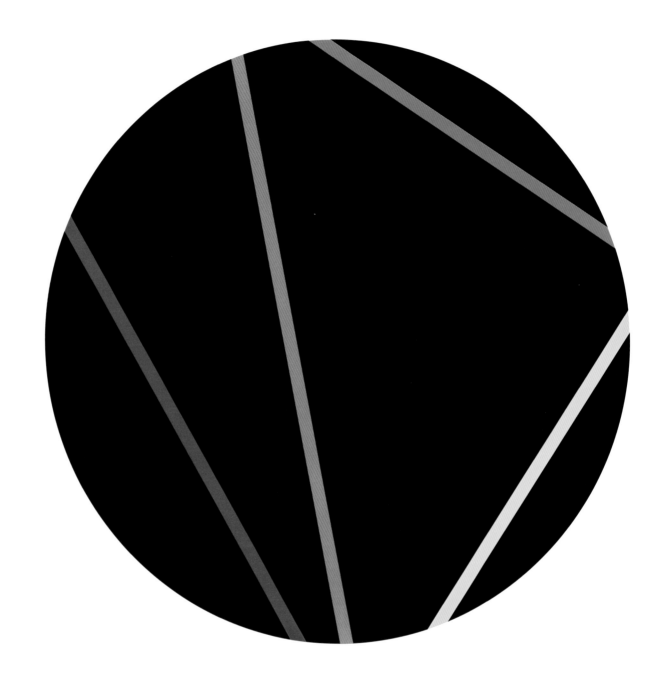

126

Circle Lines
If you cut out the disc and mounted
it on card so that you could spin it
like a top, what would you see
happen to the lines?

Circular Fit
Fit twelve disks into the circular box so that they form a tight fit with no overlapping.

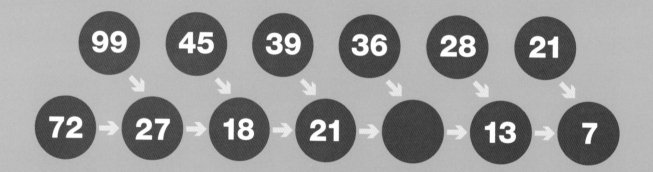

Nob's Number
There is a logic to this arrangement
of numbers. Can you work out what
the missing number should be? This
puzzle was originated by Nob
Yoshigahara.

Make Up the Difference

Distribute the numbers 1 to 15 on the circles so that the number in each circle shows the difference between the numbers in the two circles on which it sits.

129

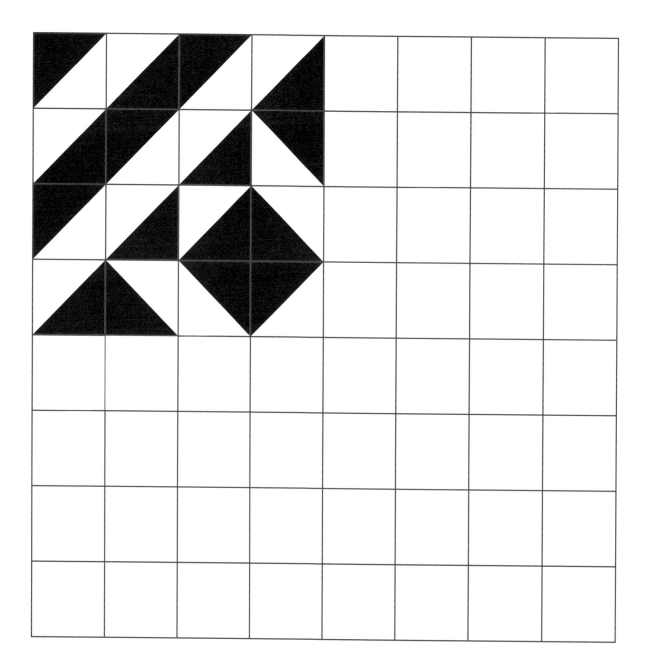

Whichever Way You Look at it
By using identical square tiles all divided diagonally into red and white, can you fill in the rest of the grid to make up a single symmetrical floor pattern?

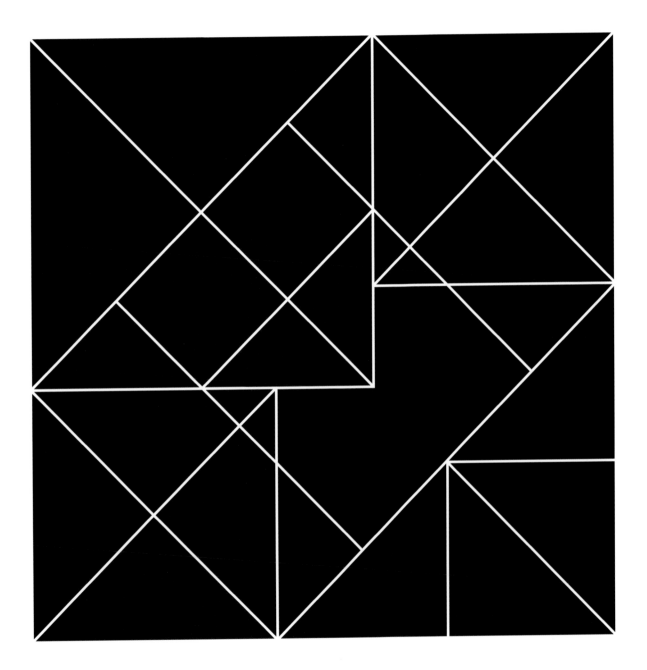

Figure Count

131

How many triangles and squares
can you find in the square pattern?

Eleven Threes
By joining any three points on a
3-by-3 peg board, can you make up
the maximum of eleven triangles?

In or Out

Which of these points are inside
and which outside this closed loop.
Rather than following the loop round
to find the answer, can you discover
a much quicker way to determine
which is inside or outside?

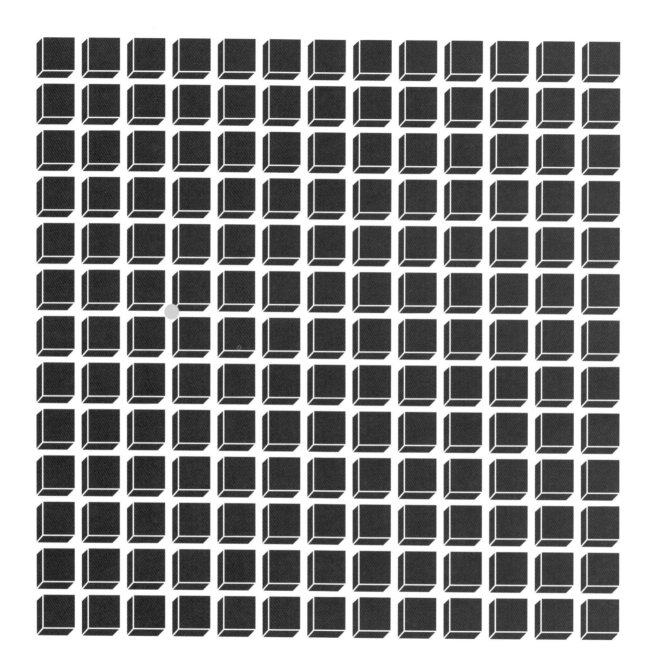

Your Original Point

Move the point so that it moves one square, turns rights, then moves two squares, turns right again, then moves three squares, turns right, and so on up to seven squares when the sequence starts again. Does the point ever come back to where it started?

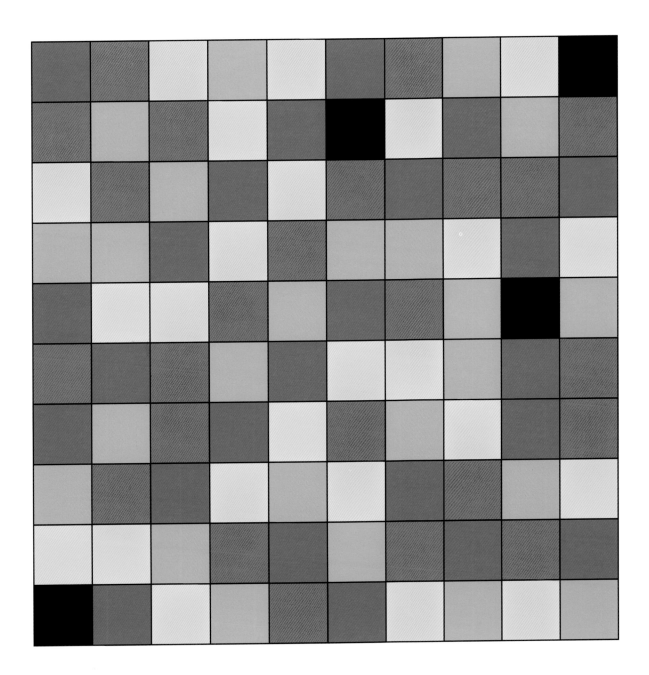

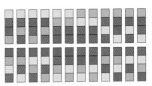

Strip Search
The 24 colour-banded strips represent 24 permutations of four numbers and four colours. The 10-by-10 gird shows an arrangement of all the strips with none overlapping, and four spare squares. Can you trace the outline of the 24 strips in the grid?

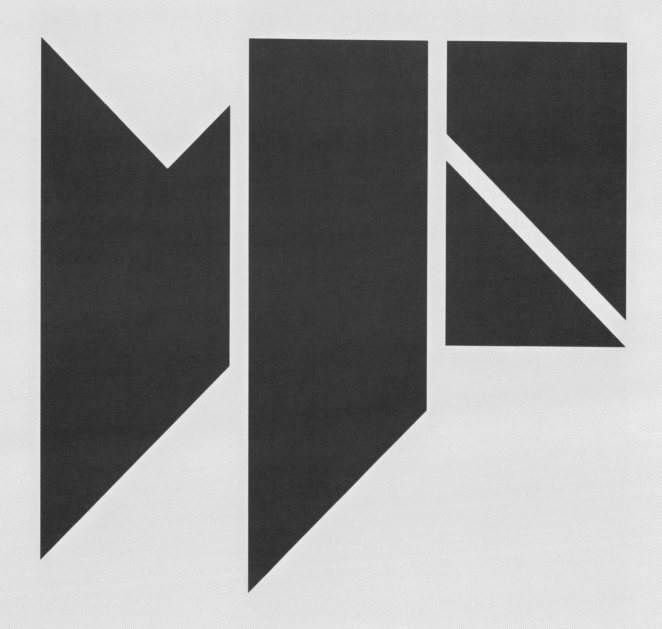

Four for T
With these four shapes can you
make up a perfect letter T?

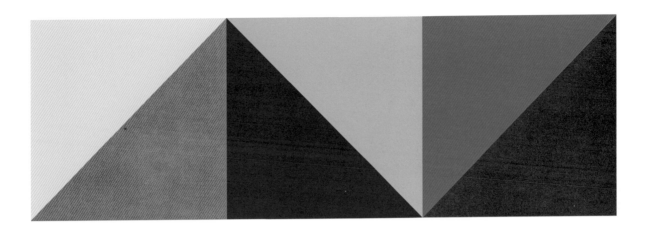

Flap Movements

Imagine a hinge connecting two adjacent corners of these triangles. By swinging one or more of the triangles, rearrange the pattern of the first square into the pattern of the second. What is the fewest number of moves required for the transformation?

String Pulling
Can you pull the string so that, first,
it makes the bobbin roll towards you
and, second, so that it makes it roll
away from you?

Breaking Point

Tie a thin thread around a heavy book. Ask someone to guess where it will break when you pull it. If the guess is that the thread will break above the book, you can pull it so that it will break below the book. If the guess is that it will break below the book, you can pull it so that it will break above the book. How do you achieve this?

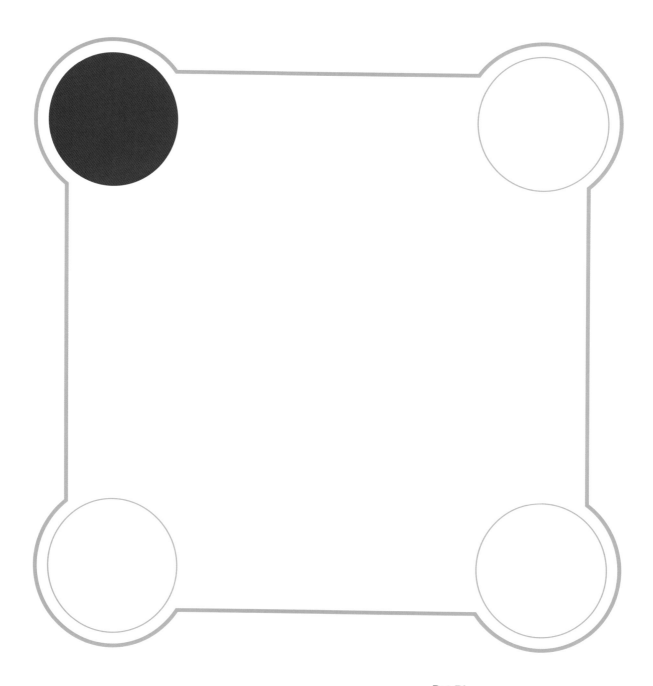

140

Pot Blue
Plot the path the ball would take
visiting three different side cushions
before dropping into the bottom
left pocket.

Two Equal Halves

This shape can be divided in half by a single line so that the two halves are exactly the same shape and size as each other. The line may be straight, angled or curved.

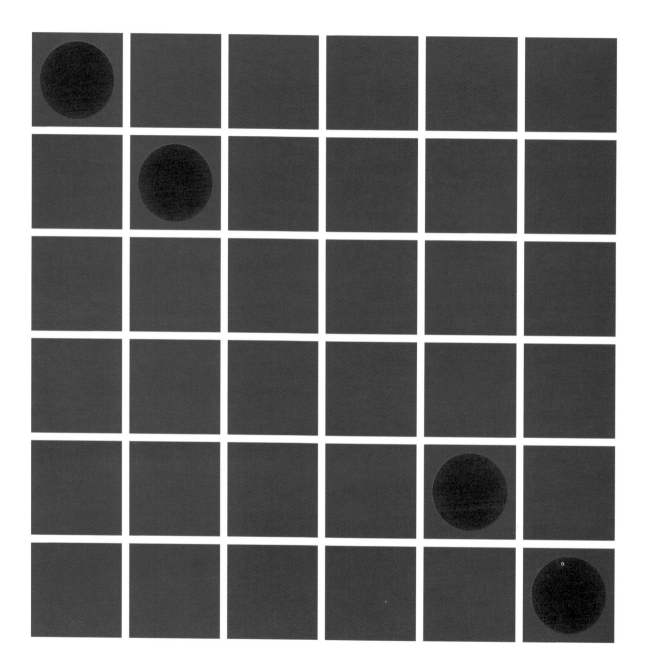

142

Reds Apart
Divide the 6-by-6 square into
four equal parts so that each part
contains one red circle.

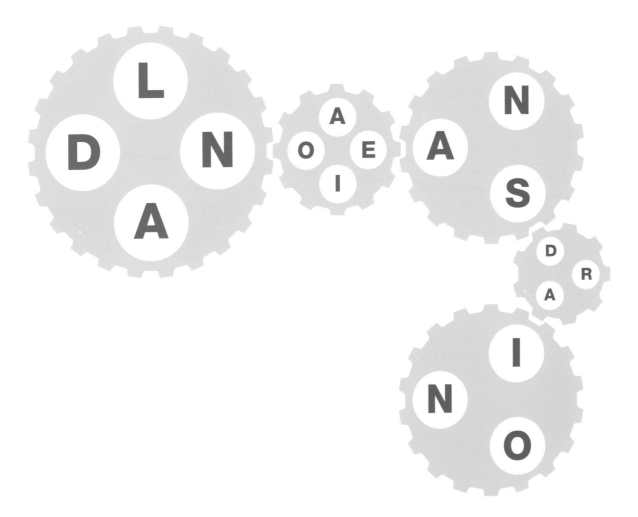

Master Word
When the interlocking gear wheels are stopped in a certain position, a word is formed by the eight letters adjacent to where the wheels touch.

(The word reads along the gear train from left to right). Work out the arrangement and find the word.

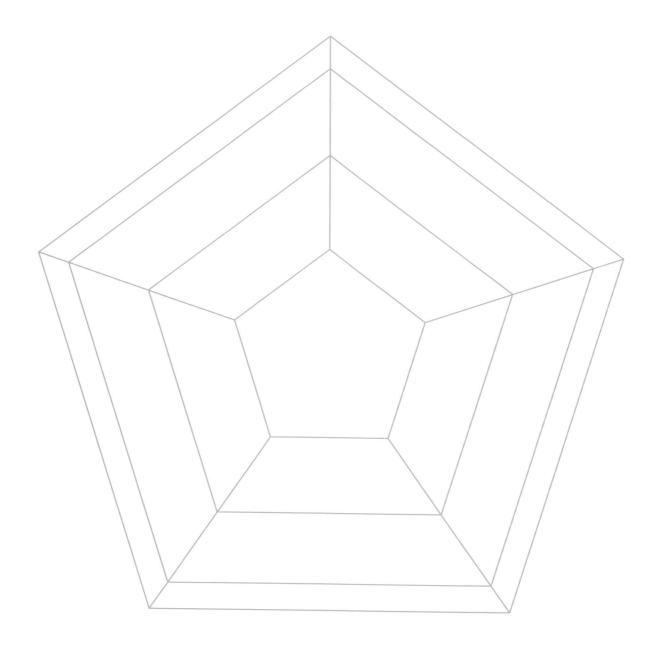

Face Colours
How many colours are needed
so that no neighbouring faces of
this two-dimensional rendition of
a dodecahedron are in the same
colour?

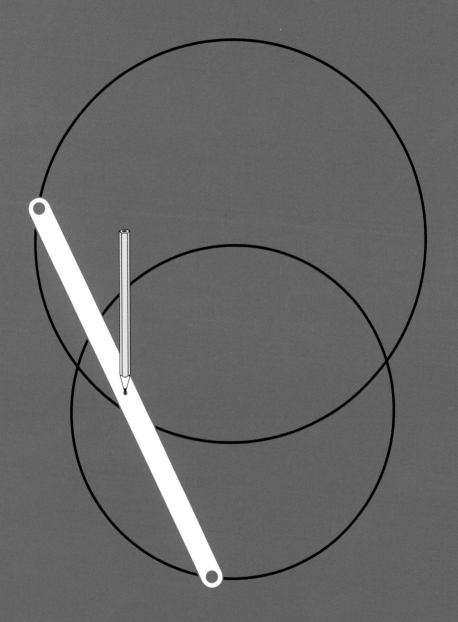

Moving Circles
Imagine a strip of card as shown.
If the two ends follow two circles
of different sizes, can you tell what
path a pencil would trace at the
middle hole?

Geometry Box

Can you find the following figures hidden in the box: four large equilateral triangles; four squares; four medium-sized equilateral triangles; eight small equilateral triangles; four half-hexagons; two irregular hexagons; one octagon; one octagram (eight-pointed star)?

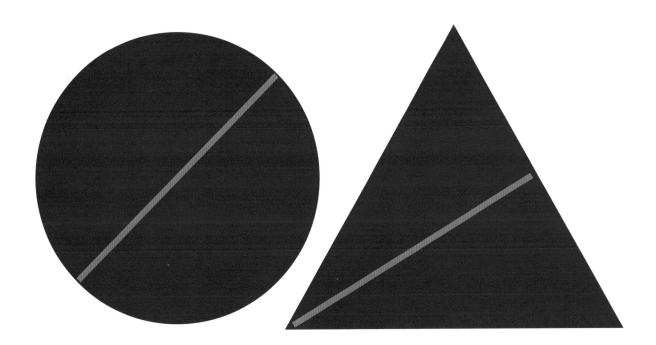

Turning Line

What is the figure of the smallest area that can contain a line of 1 unit be rotating through 360°. This can obviously be achieved in a circle; also in an equilateral triangle (the pivot point of the line does not have to be fixed).

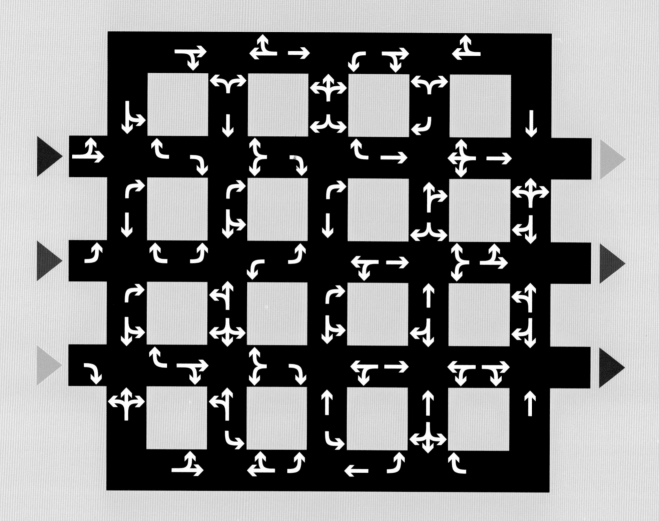

Traffic Manager

At each of these crossroads there are signs telling you which way you are allowed to go. See how easily you can get across town, first from the red entrance to the red exit, then from the blue entrance to the blue exit and finally from the green entrance to the green exit.

148

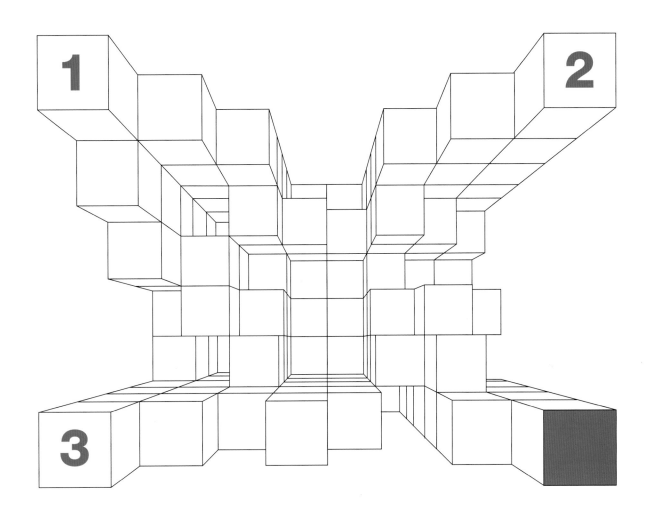

Head for the Heights

You are looking down on the four towers of a skyscraper. What route would you take to move from the numbers to the blue square in the fewest possible moves? You can move one block at a time up or down, or stay in the same plane.

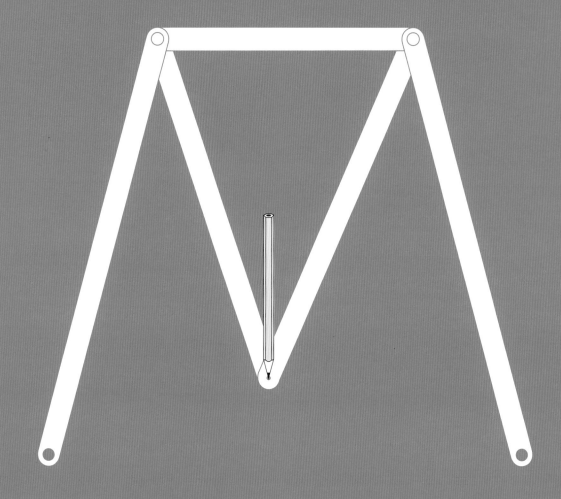

Swing Line

Cut five strips of card and make up the articulated figure laying flat on paper. The two base points are fixed and the three joints pinned so they can move. Make a hole through the centre joint and place a pencil through it onto the paper. By moving the pencil in all directions as far as it will go what path would it trace?

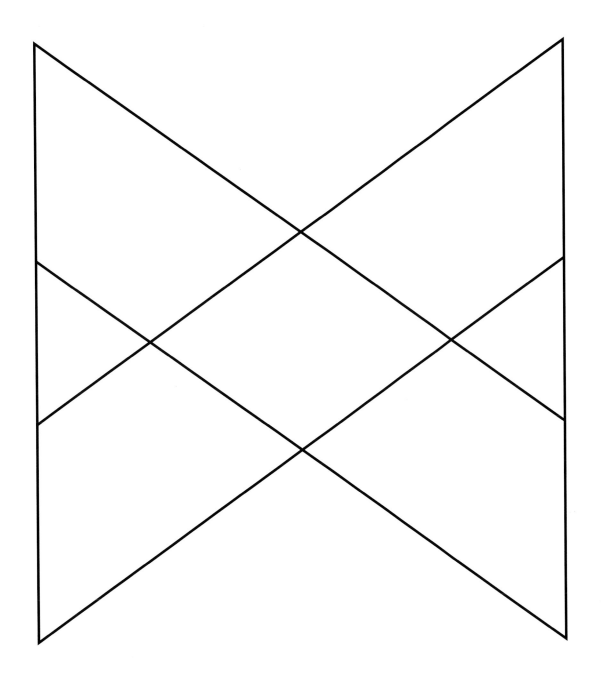

Go One Better

Eight triangles of three different sizes
are made up from this arrangement
of six lines. Can you arrange six lines
so that they make up eight triangles
of only two different sizes?

Round Head

Imagine two coins standing up side by side, as shown. If you roll the left-hand coin across the face of the right-hand coin and on to the position on the right, which way would its head be facing?

Where's the Square? 153

Draw a square so that each of the
four points lies on a different side.

Solutions

6

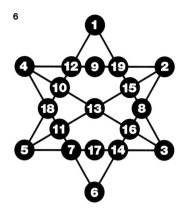

7 72 triangles.

8 1 ●, 2 ●, 3 ●, 4 ●, 5 ●, 6 ●, 7 ●, 8 ●, 9 ●, 10 ●

9 Nobody quite knows why, but the lines transform into three different sized coloured circles of a small yellow, a medium pink and a large blue.

10

11

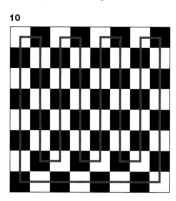

12 The figure is in fact made up from two separate pieces which could be pulled apart without cutting.

13

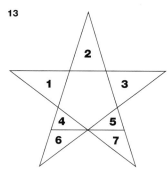

14 The chances of drawing a red ball are 40 per cent (20/50) and a blue ball 60 per cent (30/50).

15 Each circle is coloured according to the number of circles it touches.

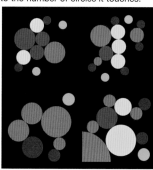

16

Day 1	4, 5, 2	7, 1, 9	6, 8, 3
Day 2	7, 5, 8	4, 3, 1	6, 9, 2
Day 3	8, 1, 2	4, 7, 6	9, 3, 5
Day 4	1, 5, 7	3, 2, 8	9, 4, 6
Day 5	8, 4, 1	5, 6, 2	3, 7, 9
Day 6	7, 2, 4	8, 9, 5	1, 6, 3

17 The numbers are alternately multiplied by 3 and divided by 2.

18 If you fold the paper into pleats you increase strength and rigidity so that it can even support a brick.

19 Take out four balls and repack the box with seven balls in the middle row. They will still make a tight fit.

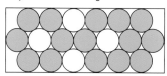

20

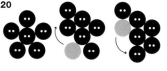

21

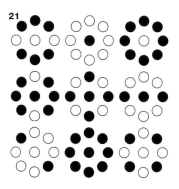

22
21 squares.

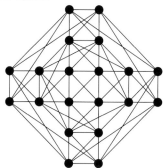

23

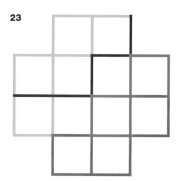

24 You have to move all the odd numbered rings to make a green radial line.

25 Pick numbers 13 and 28 to avoid elimination.

26

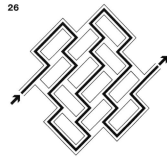

27

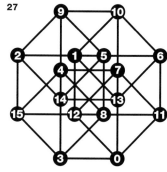

28 One weighing is sufficient. Place one red, two blue, three green, four yellow, and five pink on the scale. If the red is the odd one out it will read 15.1 oz, if the blue it will read 15.2 oz, and so on.

29

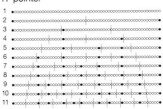

1. Circle

2. Parabola

3. Elipse

4. Hyperbola

30

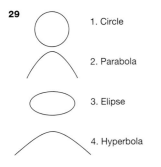

31

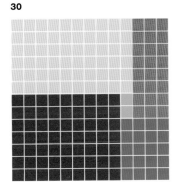

32 If you reached to line 11 placing 11 points properly you did very well. It turns out that no one can go beyond 17 points.

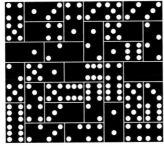

33

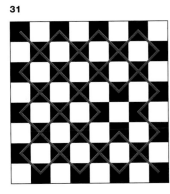

34

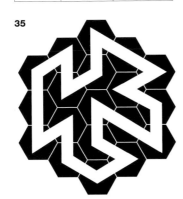

35

36

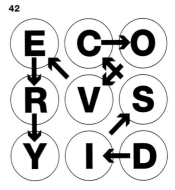

37 In the diagram 24 lines are coloured before you are forced to create a triangle of a solid colour. Can you do better?

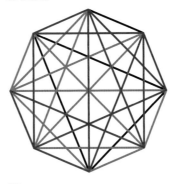

38

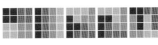

39

40 Each number is the sum of the two numbers above it.

41 50 triangles.

42

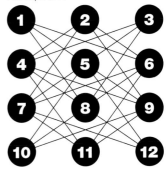

43 Move 6 to 11; 1 to 6, 8 to 1; 3 to 8, 4 to 3, 9 to 4, 10 to 9, 5 to 10, 12 to 5, 7 to 12, 2 to 7.

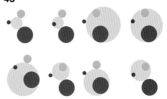

44 Either of the two middle rings.

45

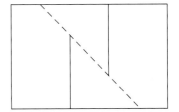

46

47

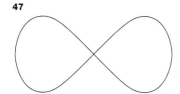

48 There are 25 prime numbers: 2, 3, 5, 7, 11, 13, 17, 19, 23, 29, 31, 37, 41, 43, 47, 53, 59, 61, 67, 71, 73, 79, 83, 89 and 97.

49

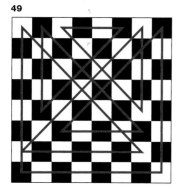

50 1. They cannot fall through their own holes accidently. 2. They can be rolled into place. 3. They do not need to be fitted into any special position.

51

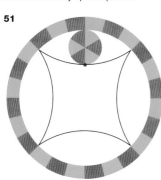

52

53 You can see six or seven cubes depending on how your brain interprets the perspective shading.

54

55

56

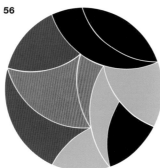

57

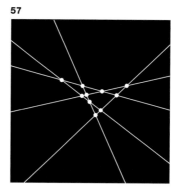

58

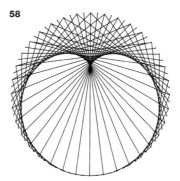

59 The lines transform into three different sized coloured circles.

60

Days	Invitations		
1	Mary	Theo	Lucy
2	Mary	Emily	David
3	Mary	John	James
4	Mary	Kate	Jane
5	Theo	Emily	John
6	Theo	David	John
7	Theo	James	Kate
8	Lucy	Emily	James
9	Lucy	David	Kate
10	Lucy	John	Jane
11	Emily	Kate	Jane
12	David	James	Jane

61 ONE WORD

62

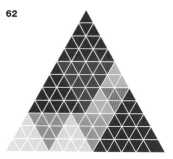

63

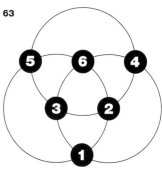

64 Each number is the sum of the two preceding numbers. As the sequence continues it approaches the Golden Section as represented here in the Golden Rectangle, where the two sides bear this 'divine' relationship to one another – 1:1.6180037. Organic growth in plants and animals follows this rule. For instance the logarithmic spiral contained by the rectangles follows the same growth pattern as a snail shell.

65

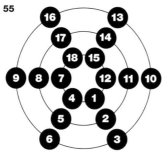

66

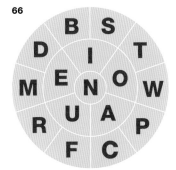

67

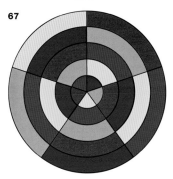

68 16 different ways.

69

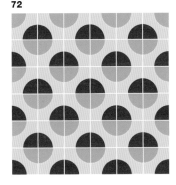

70

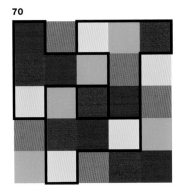

71

ABCDEFG HIJKLMN OPQRST UVWXYZ

72

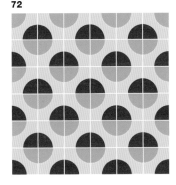

73

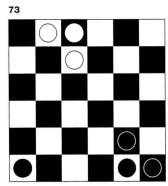

74

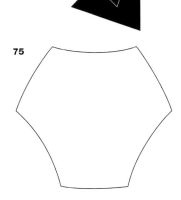

75

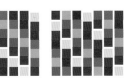

76 CONDUCTION

77 Number 1 is the smallest number of persistence. 2, 3, 4 and 5 are the numbers of persistence for 25, 39, 77 and 679 respectively. Every starting number leads to a single digit, the process is not infinite.

78

79 Missing cubes: 1 cube coloured on three sides, 6 cubes coloured on two sides, 12 cubes coloured on one side, 7 cubes with no colour.

80 Isoceles triangle – 2 ways; Scalene triangle – 1 way; Equilateral triangle – 6 ways; Square – 8 ways; Swiss cross – 8 ways; Rhombus – 4 ways; Parallelogram – 2 ways; – Tetrahedron – 12 ways; Cube – 24 ways.

81
Anti-clockwise   Clockwise

82

83

84

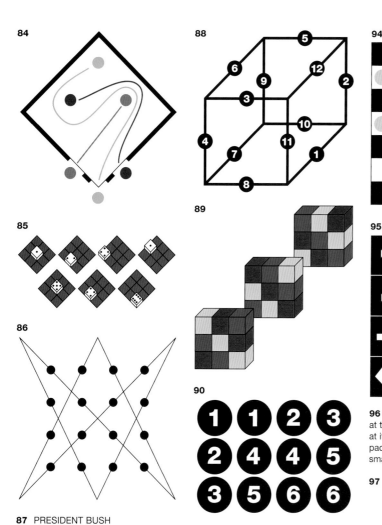

85

86

87 PRESIDENT BUSH

88

89

90

91 1+2+3-4+5+6+78+9 =100
There are many different solutions.

92 Place the glass over the marble and move it round and round so that the marble starts to spin around inside of the glass. When you have got the marble spinning fast enough you can lift the jar off the table. The marble will not drop out immediately as it continues to spin around under its own momentum.

93 6 pieces of string.

94

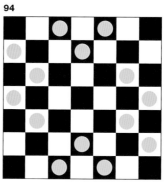

95

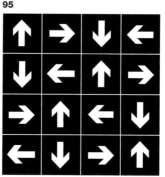

96 Actually, the biggest apples end up at the top because the arrangement is at its most stable with the most densely packed apples, which will be the smaller apples, at the bottom.

97

98

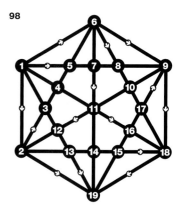

99 One of the many possible solutions.

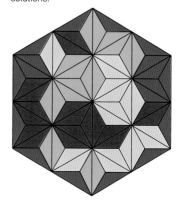

100 The values of the radii of the resulting circle approach a limit of approximately 12 times that of the original circle.

101

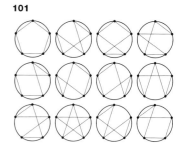

102

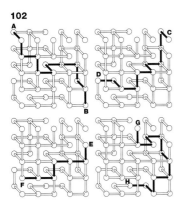

103 52 triangles.

104

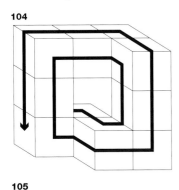

105

16	12	8	4
15	11	7	3
14	10	6	2
13	9	5	1

106

$$16-5+2=13$$
$$2 \times 15 \div 3 = 10$$
$$11+7=14+4$$
$$12 = 8 \times 9 \div 6$$

107 The numbers of letters in each successive word of the question make up a sequence. So the answer is the number of letters in the last word.

108

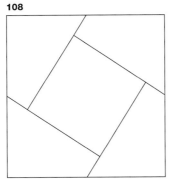

109 Actually the area of the green square has been taken up by subtracting a line of negligible thickness all the way round the whole outer square. The difference is so small you can't see it.

110

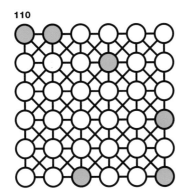

111

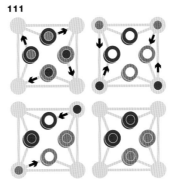

112

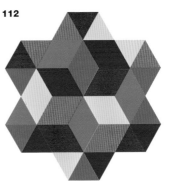

113

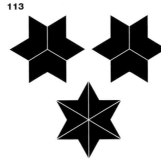

114

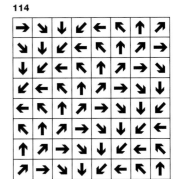

115 There are a number of shortest routes the drivers could take.

116

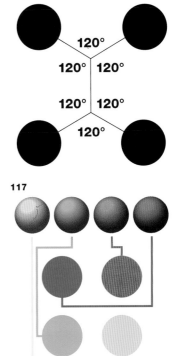

117

118 Two of the squares in the centre are fixed; the other three move round them clockwise.

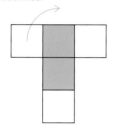

119 Green cannot be connected to make a continuous line.

120

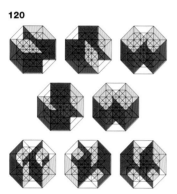

121 9 hexagons.

122 4, 10, 15, 20, 26, 30 will be the first to be eliminated.

123

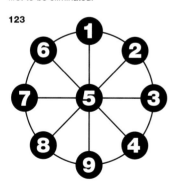

124 One of the possible colour matching configurations using 19 out of the 20 hexagons.

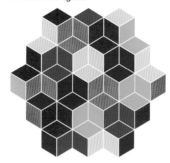

125

126 This baffling illusion creates concentric circles out of the straight lines when the disc is spinning. Nobody is quite sure why. And although there are four lines, you see only three circles.

127

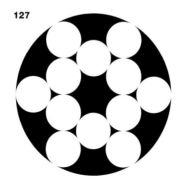

128 You might think the answer is 15. Think again. The right answer is 12. (And, yes, the last circle number is not a misprint; it really should be 7, not 8.)

129

130

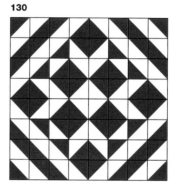

131 44 triangles, 7 squares.

132

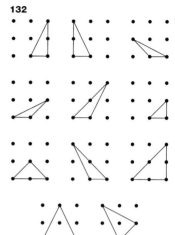

133 From each point draw a straight line to the outside. Count the number of intersections. If the number is odd the point is inside. If the number is even the point is outside.

134

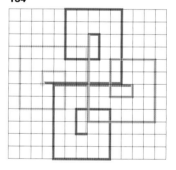

135

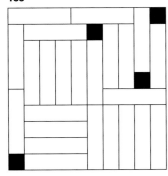

136

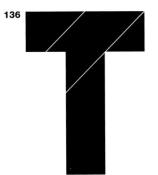

137

138

It all depends on the angle of the string. Pulling up at an angle creates a torque that turns the bobbin away from you. Pulling with the string at a much lower angle creates an opposite torque which makes it roll towards you.

139 When you pull on the lower hand slowly and firmly the additional weight of the book on the thread above the book means it will break there. But if you pull quickly you momentarily overcome the book's inertia so that the tension is less in the upper part of the thread, and it will break below the book.

140

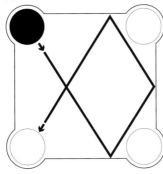

141

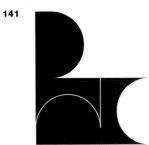

142

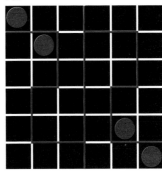

143 'LEONARDO' DA VINCI

144

145

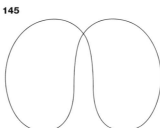

146

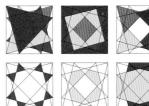
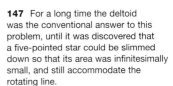

147 For a long time the deltoid was the conventional answer to this problem, until it was discovered that a five-pointed star could be slimmed down so that its area was infinitesimally small, and still accommodate the rotating line.

148

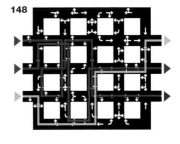

149

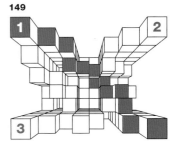

150 A straight line.

151

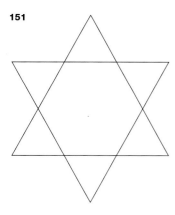

152 The head on the coin would not, as you think, be upside down. It would end up facing to the left again.

153

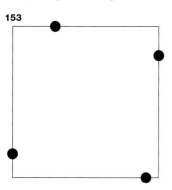

Acknowledgements
First and foremost, I would like to express my deep gratitude to my wife Anitta, for her enduring support and patience; and to my daughter Hila, for her encouragement, great ideas and honest censorship.

My appreciation and thanks to Martin Gardner, Harry Lindren, Professor Richard Gregory, Ian Stewart, David Singmaster, Nob Yoshigahara, Edward Hordern, Jerry Slocum, James Dalgety, Laurie Brokenshire, Mark Setteducati, Tim Rowett, and many others…

Last but not least, it is a great privilege for me to join this exciting series by David Hillman of Pentagram, which translates so well abstract ideas of mathematics into beautiful works of art.

Ivan Moscovich
March 1994, London

Pentagram is one of the world's leading design groups with an international reputation in graphic design, product design and architecture. It has grown consistently since starting with five partners in 1972. Today there are 18 partners and over 100 staff in the London, New York and San Francisco offices. Amongst its many clients are Lloyd's of London, Arthur Anderson, Boots, Tate Gallery, Coca Cola, Four Seasons Hotel Group, Kenwood, and Polaroid.

David Hillman compiled and designed the original *Puzzlegrams* which was published in1989. *Pentagames* followed in 1990 and *Phantasmagrams* in 1992. In the 1960s and 70s he made his name as an editorial designer and art director on the *Sunday Times Magazine, Nova,* and *Le Matin de Paris*. He became a Pentagram partner in 1978 where he broadened his design output to include corporate and non-editorial graphics, retail design, signs and packaging. He was responsible for the redesigning of the award-winning *Guardian* newspaper in 1988. He has won a number of D&AD awards and is currently the UK President of the Alliance Graphique Internationale.

As a mathematician, engineer, artist, and inventor Ivan Moscovich has been collecting, designing, creating and inventing puzzles, games, toys and educational aids for over thirty years. He is one of a unique group of people around the world of many different professions and backgrounds sharing a fascination with mind games and who feed each other with ideas as well as enthusiasm in their enjoyment of recreational mathematics and geometry. His other work has included the conception and creation of hands-on exhibitions for the Lasky Museum of Science, Technology, and Planetarium. He has lived and worked in London since 1989.